FRISIAN
PILOT

FRISIAN PILOT

Den Helder to Brunsbüttel and the Kiel Canal

Mark Brackenbury

Charts designed by the author
and drawn by E. H. Wilson

STANFORD MARITIME   LONDON

Stanford Maritime Limited
Member Company of the George Philip Group
12 Long Acre   London WC2E 9LP

First published in Great Britain 1979
Copyright © Mark Brackenbury 1979

Set in 11/12 Times by
Malvern Typesetting Services Limited
Printed and bound in Great Britain by
R. J. Acford Limited
Chichester, Sussex

British Library Cataloguing in Publication Data

Brackenbury, Mark
    Frisian pilot.
    1. Pilot guides—Netherlands—Friesland
    2. Pilot guides—Netherlands—Groningen (Province)
    3. Pilot guides—Germany, West—Saxony, Lower
    I. Title
    623.89'29'4921   VK825

ISBN 0-540-07185-4

To the Cruising Association

Contents

APPENDICES

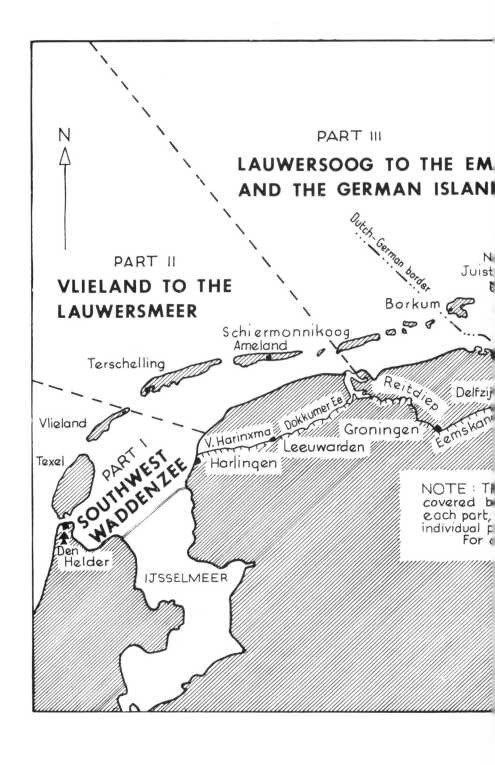

N

PART III

LAUWERSOOG TO THE EM
AND THE GERMAN ISLANI

Dutch-German border

N
Juist

Borkum

PART II

VLIELAND TO THE
LAUWERSMEER

Schiermonnikoog
Ameland

Terschelling

Reitdiep

Delfzij

Vlieland

Dokkumer Ee

Groningen

Eemskan

Texel

V. Harinxma

Leeuwarden

PART I

SOUTHWEST

WADDENZEE

Harlingen

NOTE: T
covered b
each part,
individual p
For

Den
Helder

IJSSELMEER

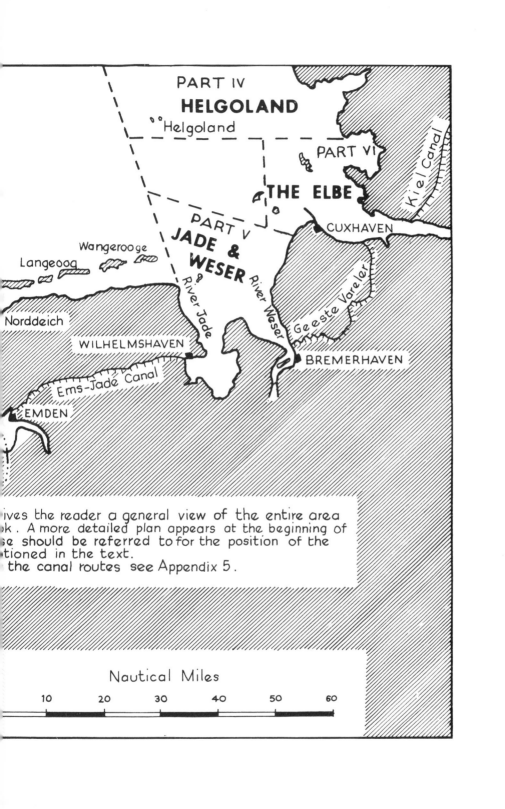

PART IV
HELGOLAND
° °Helgoland

PART VI

THE ELBE

CUXHAVEN

PART V
JADE &
WESER

Wangerooge

Langeoog

River Jade

River Weser

Geeste Varel er

Norddeich

WILHELMSHAVEN

Ems-Jade Canal

BREMERHAVEN

EMDEN

Kiel Canal

...ives the reader a general view of the entire area
...k. A more detailed plan appears at the beginning of
...se should be referred to for the position of the
...tioned in the text.
...the canal routes see Appendix 5.

Nautical Miles

10   20   30   40   50   60

Introduction

It has always seemed surprising that no pilot book existed in English to cover the Frisian area, as it is not only a fascinating cruising ground in its own right, but is also regularly visited by British yachts on their way to the Kiel Canal and a Baltic cruise. I hope that this book will be of value both to the passage-maker and to the visitor who is prepared to take the time to explore the inshore waters of the area, and that it may indeed encourage others to visit the area for the first time.

The waters are shallow and the channels shift, but on the other hand they are profusely marked and the position of the channel indicators is kept meticulously up to date, so once the general principles of marking are understood navigation of the area presents few problems. In a windy summer the sheltered waters inside the Frisian chain provide a huge area where sailing can be enjoyed even by those who would otherwise be suffering from the scourge of seasickness.

It seems appropriate to finish this short introduction on a note of scholarship. The Dutch part of the region is mainly known as Friesland, and the German part as Ostfriesland, while the language (it is more than a dialect) which is spoken on the islands on both sides of the border is Fries. In spite of this, three dictionaries and one encyclopaedia which I have consulted unanimously declare that the correct adjective (in English) is 'Frisian'. 'Friesian', one gathers, is strictly reserved for the cow!

This is, however, no more than a matter of interest: nobody is likely to be irritated if you spell Frisian with an e. But some Dutchmen *do* get irritated, and with some reason, by the English habit of calling their country Holland, and apart from being irritating it can often be confusing. Originally known as the United Provinces, the Kingdom of the Netherlands today consists of ten

Provinces: Groningen, Friesland, Overijssel, Gelderland, Utrecht, Noord Holland, Zuid Holland, Zeeland, Noord Brabant and Limburg. Noord and Zuid Holland together are properly called Holland, that is the part of the Netherlands extending from the Hook of Holland (hence its name: *hoek* means corner) in the south to Den Helder in the north. This book is concerned mainly with Friesland and Groningen.

It is of course common English usage to refer to the whole country as Holland, and it does no harm over here, but you can imagine how you would feel if a foreigner persisted in referring to England as Yorkshire. Apart from the annoyance which this must cause, genuine confusion can arise if you say to a yachtsman in Delfzijl (Province of Groningen), 'I am always glad when I get back to Holland.' You intend a compliment, but he thinks that you are looking forward to getting out of his province and back to another!

I do not expect readers to change the habits of a lifetime overnight, but at least this note may enable the worst of the traps to be avoided.

Cruising in Friesland

From Den Helder, the port where our coverage begins, the Frisian Islands form a fringe which protects the mainland coast for the 150 miles or so to the estuary of the Elbe. A similar chain also runs up the west coast of Jutland, north of the Elbe, but falls outside the scope of this book. At the western end the Frisian islands lie as much as fifteen miles offshore, but this distance grows less further east, and some of the German islands lie only a couple of miles from the mainland.

The waters inside the Dutch islands are known as the Waddenzee, from the Fries word *wad*, meaning a mudflat. Some authors confine the use of the name to the wide waters inshore of Texel, Vlieland and Terschelling, but it correctly describes the inshore waters as far east as the Ems and the German border. There does not seem to be any comparable German term, but the banks there are known as *Watten*, clearly from the same root.

In the wide waters of the west Waddenzee there are a few through channels that can be navigated at low water, because of the faster and more complex tidal streams. Even here, however, many of the most useful channels dry at low water, and this is typical of the waters further east. These channels are known in Dutch as *vaarwateren*, and as *Fahrwassern* in German.

To understand the system of tides and channels, one must remember that the flood tide makes along the coast from west to east (HW Texel is about $4\frac{1}{2}$ hours earlier than HW Wangerooge). So the young flood reaches the gap to the west of an island some time before that to the east. Once in, it fans out behind the island, but by the time it has started flowing through the gap to the east, the tide from the west will have had a start of as much as twenty minutes.

For this reason, the flood streams always meet not at the middle of an island, but about a third of its length from its eastern end.

Along this line there is never any stream to speak of, as the opposing floods or ebbs are always in balance. As a result, silt carried up by the flood deposits and builds up, in places almost to the high water level. The line of the watershed is known in Dutch as the *wantij* (weak-tide) bank, and in German as the *Wattenhoch*, and to sail from the west to the east end of an island involves the crossing of at least one of these.

The water in the gap between each island (which I will refer to as appropriate by the Dutch word *zeegat* or the German *Seegat*), is deep, and there is usually deep water some distance towards the watershed. Then even the best channel becomes shallower, usually drying by up to a metre at LWS. Where deep, the channels are often buoyed, but the shallower parts are marked by withies: saplings inserted into the sand along the edge of the channel at low water. These are known as *pricken* in both Dutch and German. (An earnest German yachtsman never knew why I laughed when he clutched my arm and said, 'Do not trust the pricks in Langeoog harbour: they are very unreliable!') Normal saplings in their natural state (twigs pointing up) are used as IALA port-hand lateral markers, which means that in the main channels they are on the north side of the channel. More rarely, starboard markers are used: these are made by breaking off the twigs from the stem of the sapling, and tying them on again pointing downward. For normal saplings I will use the term withies: for the starboard-hand variety I will adopt the English word besom, from their Dutch name *bezem* (the Germans call them *Kopfpricken*). This seems suitably descriptive, and I have to coin a word as I cannot find that they have ever been described in English before. The symbols for withies are very similar on Dutch and German charts, but different for besoms. However, be warned that for many channels only the withy symbol is used although both kinds of marker may in fact be found. Besoms are never laid without good reason, so it is most important to pay attention to the difference, and leave them on the starboard side (by IALA definition) when they are met.

Dutch pricken

German

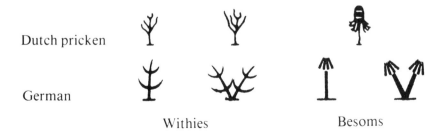

Withies   Besoms

I must point out here that the IALA buoyage behind the islands adopts the convention that the Main Flood Stream runs from west to east throughout the area, regardless of the actual facts. Thus all the main channels to the east have port-hand buoys on their north sides even after the watershed has been passed, and the flood stream is now west-going. This avoids the problem of changing buoyage in midstream, but is confusing if you are coming in from seaward (when port-hand buoys are left to port) and then proceeding up a westbound channel, when they suddenly have to be left to starboard!

There are of course several cross-channels where it is impossible to tell whether they are north-to-south or south-to-north flood channels: on the Dutch Yacht Charts the direction of the (theoretical) flood is marked by large red outlined arrows; in German waters the system can only be deduced by careful examination of the chart in question. This is usually, but not always, easy enough: I have just once or twice been reduced to sounding my way round a buoy to find out which side the deeper water is, but this is only likely to happen after a major shift in the route of one of the very minor channels.

One would need detailed local knowledge before deliberately setting out to cross a watt at night, but it is useful to know in case of emergency that, at least in the major channels, the withies each carry a ring of reflective red plastic, which makes them very easy to pick up in the beam of a torch. I have often made use of this fact to enable me to risk finishing a crossing just after dark when the tide was inconveniently late, but I repeat, do not try this until at least you know the lie of the channel!

To cross one watt, the ideal is obviously to arrive at the watershed at local HW (high water), bearing in mind that this will be half an hour or so later than HW at the zeegat to the east. Timing it in this way, one will have a gentle flood helping one up to the watershed, and the first of the ebb carrying one down the other side. However, with moderate draft and reliable engine power, it is quite possible to cross more than one watt on a tide: indeed, with 1.25 m draft I have twice run one tide all the way from Langeoog to the Ems, crossing no less than four watersheds on the way. This did admittedly depend on motoring fast and cutting every possible corner, and it was always a comfort to know that I was a bilge-keeler, so that if I didn't make it, we would at least spend the night sitting upright.

To cross more than one watt, always leave early enough. Except in really rough weather there is seldom much sea near the watershed, because the channel is surrounded by even shallower water, so if there is not yet enough water to cross it is often safe to run gently

The watt at low water. The fishing boat at the left is leaving
Dornumersiel with the last of the water.

aground and wait, pushing softly with the engine, until the tide
allows you to slide across. With moderate draft this usually leaves
plenty of time to reach and cross the next watershed on the same
tide, often still before high water. In rough weather, or on exceptionally exposed passages like the Hohe Weg, it is safer to jill
about or anchor until there is enough water to cross without risking a
bump on what is often very hard sand. The echosounder should be
used constantly, at least until a good deal of experience of the waters
has been acquired, and it is as well to remember that the channels
wind tortuously, far more than appears from the charts, which give
only a general indication, so it is seldom possible to make a whole
crossing without occasional help from the engine, even when the
overall direction is downwind.

While following the channel, it is useful to remember that the
withies are inserted more or less along the low-water line. The effect
of this is that as the channel gets shallower, the best water approaches the marks more closely. Thus at the start of a channel one
may find the best water twenty metres or more away from the
withies, but near the watershed it may be no more than two or three
metres from them. This is of course usually only critical when trying

to cross very early or rather late on a tide, but the knowledge can sometimes make the difference between success and failure. Depths on the main watersheds are generally $1\frac{1}{2}$ to 2 m at HW neaps, with about 0.3 m more at HW springs, so it will be seen that this is not a cruising area for the deep-draft yacht: I would say that 1.6 m is the maximum draft for actually cruising the inshore channels, though of course the main harbours can be used on passage by yachts of any draft.

The ideal craft is of course the bilge-keeled yacht, or one with a centreboard passing through a keel short enough to allow the boat to stand more or less upright when dried out. This is important not only if you make an error of navigation and have to spend a tide on a sandbank, but also because it saves a lot of bother in the harbours which dry partly or wholly. It is also a tradition in the area to picnic by simply running on a bank at half ebb, and swimming from one's private desert island as it is revealed by the receding tide.

But do not let the above discourage the owner of a keelboat from visiting the area. Several of my Dutch friends cruise these waters in keel designs; one couple I know have visited almost every island in their Rival 34, which draws $1\frac{1}{2}$ m. It is just necessary to be a little more careful, and to plan the cruise so that only one or two watts have to be crossed on a tide, and if possible so that extreme neaps are spent in the deeper parts of the cruising ground.

Above all, the Frisians are a place for the yachtsman who likes sometimes to get away from civilization, and is not afraid of a night at anchor in the lee of an island with only a few scattered lights to show where there are houses ashore, and the whistle of an oyster-catcher for company.

It is often pleasant to cross a watt at dusk, and then anchor once over the watershed and back in deep water. These deeps are usually surrounded by banks that only cover near HW, and so as the tide falls one can lie in perfect safety and shelter, sometimes even out of sight of land, until the next high tide in the morning. But rig an anchor light: fishermen often work their way up these channels in the dark.

Streams are not strong over the watts, but can be very fierce in the zeegats. I am told that rates can attain 5 knots in the Dove Harle, and 3 or 4 knots is commonplace along the coast. With an onshore wind, vicious seas occur in these entrances during the ebb, even with winds as light as force 4, and as few sailing yachts have the power to motor out against both the wind and a 4 knot flood, it can be impossible to get out into the North Sea for days at a time. However, this is seldom serious for the British yachtsman, as he can always

17

Typical sailing conditions on the watt. This was taken between
Norderney and Baltrum in force 6–7: note the lack of any real
sea.

make for home by the inshore route if time is running out. The
Marsdiep at Den Helder can be used in any weather, as can the
Westerems; the next easiest exits are probably the Stortemelk at
Terschelling and the Dove Tief at Norderney, but both of these can
be very rough even in moderate weather from the wrong quarter.

So much for the Frisian Islands and the inshore waters. Helgoland
offers the most complete contrast possible: a deep-water harbour
available at all states of the tide and in all weathers, and loomed over
by a considerable mountain. It is beset by trippers during the day,
being the German fiscal equivalent of the Channel Islands, but is
quiet at night, and offers a good harbour and a most valuable port
of refuge.

Finally, the eastern rivers, the Elbe, Weser and Jade. The Elbe is
the gateway to the Kiel Canal (Nord-Ostsee Kanal in German), but
all three suffer from very high and dangerous seas with an onshore
wind over the ebb tide. It can therefore be extremely difficult for a
small yacht to get out, and it is always wise for skippers with

schedules to meet to allow for the possibility of a couple of days' delay on the way home.

CHARTS

I regret to say that for the exploring yachtsman, the charts issued by the British Admiralty cannot be recommended except for Helgoland and perhaps the Elbe. Very little inshore buoyage is shown, and the lie of the lesser channels is indicated, if at all, only by the words 'buoyed channel' printed across several miles. It is far better to use the charts published in the countries concerned. An excellent coverage can be achieved as follows:

Dutch chart 1454 (South Waddenzee, Den Helder-Harlingen)

Dutch chart 1456 (North Waddenzee, Harlingen, Vlieland, Terschelling)

Dutch chart 1458 (East Terschelling—Schiermonnikoog with the Lauwersmeer)

There is then a choice, as far as the Ems and outlying islands is concerned, of:

Dutch 1460 or German 90 (Schiermonnikoog, Juist and outer Ems)

Dutch 1555 or German 91 (Inner Ems with Delfzijl and Emden)

After which the remaining area would be covered by German charts:

89 (Juist to West Wangerooge)

 2 (Jade and Weser entrance and approaches to Elbe)

 7 (Inner Jade with Hooksiel, and Wilhelmshaven)

 4 (Weser to Bremerhaven)

44 (Outer Elbe to Cuxhaven)

45 (Inner Elbe, Cuxhaven to Brunsbüttel)

88 (Helgoland: not really necessary as adequately shown in this book, except for entrance from the north)

These are all large-scale charts, and do not cover the open sea passages offshore. At least one addition, German chart 49, is needed to connect Helgoland into the system: it covers Helgoland, the mouths of the three eastern rivers, and the German islands as far as east Baltrum.

One major alternative is to use the Yacht Charts (*Kaart voor Zeil-en Motorjachten*) published by the Dutch Hydrographic Office in bound 'booklet' form. These offer several advantages: they are a convenient size for the smaller yacht (53 x 36 cm), they are fully coloured (buoys, light sectors and water depths), and they have more and better plans of harbours. However, while offshore passages can be made with the conventional separate sea charts listed above, they cannot with the Yacht Chart booklets, and one would need to carry British Admiralty 2593 (Zeegat van Texel to Friesche Zeegat) to make up. But still, the virtues of the Yacht Charts (which also carry English translations of Dutch terms, abbreviations and symbols) are considerable. They are not corrected between printing and issue, but under normal conditions this makes little or no difference, and old copies can be corrected by the owner from *Notices to Mariners* or other sources in exactly the same way as sea charts. Two sets are needed to cover our area: 1811 (Waddenzee Westblad) and 1812 (Waddenzee Oostblad). If these are chosen, German charts 90 and 91 can be omitted.

As I mentioned above, British charts of the Elbe are satisfactory as a substitute, as long as there is no intention of trying the watt-passage to the Weser. With an up-to-date edition of this book it should also be safe to dispense with the large-scale Helgoland chart, and the intrepid may be prepared to omit German chart 44, jumping from 2 to 45: there is a gap of about 7 miles in the coverage, but it is closely covered with straightforward IALA lateral buoyage. No. 44 is also needed if the Elbe-Weser watt-passage is contemplated.

As with the Dutch Yacht Charts (but not sea charts), the German sea charts carry English translations of abbreviations. *Reed's Almanac* gives a useful glossary of foreign chart terms. *Born's Schipperskaart* of the Dutch canals should also be carried in case the system has to be used, perhaps because of bad weather. The ANWB *Waterkaarten* provide a detailed coverage, and there is a useful key to these and the Dutch Yacht Charts, *Vaarwaterkaart van Nederland*, published by the ANWB.

The best chart stockist in the UK is J. D. Potter Ltd, 145 The Minories, London EC3N 1NH. They may well have the Dutch Yacht Charts and *Born's* in stock, and will obtain the others to order. German charts are also available on order through Imray's, Wych House, St Ives, Huntingdon, Cambs. *Born's*, guides for Continental inland waters, and yachtsmen's 'pilots' are also stocked by Stanfords, 12–14 Long Acre, London WC2E 9LP. Within the area, the outstanding chart agent is Datema, Oude Schans 11, Delfzijl. They keep very full stocks of Dutch, German and British charts, and readers may well find it worth postponing the purchase of the German portfolio until they reach Delfzijl, as they tend to be cheaper there than in the UK. Another excellent bet is L. J. Harri, Prins Hendrikkade 90, Amsterdam, which may easily be visited on the way; also Fritz H. Venske, 2981 Norddeich (just above the yacht harbour), keeps good stocks of German charts.

One eccentricity of all the charts in this area is worth mentioning. When a major change in the run of a channel takes place, the next edition of the chart will have the *buoys* printed in their new positions, but the underlying contour lines showing the bottom are not altered until a new survey is carried out. One may therefore find charts where the buoys appear to go over shallow water or drying sand, with an unmarked deep-water channel nearby. In fact, of course, what has happened is that the channel has shifted to a new position, and the buoys have been moved to mark it. This movement has been recorded on the plate which prints the buoys on the chart, but there has not yet been time to re-draw the plate for the bottom contours. This is an extreme case of an important general principle, which must be clearly grasped: in any area of shifting sands the chart shows the overall shape of the channels, and the system of buoyage, but is likely to be inaccurate in detail. If a channel shown straight on the chart has a kink in its buoyage, do not try to cut across: the extra buoy will not have been put there for fun! And do not hope that by measuring the lie of a channel on the chart you know its length: many are far more intricate than can be shown on the scale of a chart, and thus also far longer. So observation, common sense, seamanship and regular sounding are all vital if a cruise in this area is to be enjoyable and troublefree.

TIDES AND TIDAL STREAMS

Particularly in the SW Waddenzee, the tidal streams are very complex, and can only be followed with the aid of a detailed stream atlas. Full details of these tidal atlases, and many other facts and figures on the tides in the area, are to be found in Appendix 4.

For the purpose of this introduction it is enough to give a few general facts. In the SW Waddenzee the flood pours in first past Den Helder, and then successively through the zeegats further NE. The first flood-waters meet SW of Harlingen near Kornwerderzand, but soon the meetingplace moves to the Terschelling wantij bank (watershed), where it remains for the rest of the flood. The ebb divides at this bank also, so it can be regarded as the high water mark for the tidal system in the SW Waddenzee.

Further east, the tides behave reasonably predictably, flowing behind the islands as already explained, and changing in the eastern rivers at near enough the times of local high and low water, which can be found in local tide tables or calculated from the tidal differences listed in Appendix 4.

One vital point, however, must be mentioned. With W or NW winds, particularly when they are well established, the mean level of the waters in the whole area will be raised, often by as much as 0.3 m. Similarly, winds between NE and E will *lower* the mean level by a similar amount. **All figures given later in this book for depths of water at High Water Springs or Neaps are for average conditions: in established strong easterly winds these figures must be reduced by at least 0.3 metres for safety.** The German weather services do provide forecast figures for these variations, but I have always found that if one works on a rule of thumb that force 6 westerly and easterly winds give 0.3 m more or less water respectively, with the effect going up to 0.4 or even 0.5 m in gales, and down to 0.2 m for force 4 or 5, that is about as accurate as you are ever likely to need.

AMENITIES

The Dutch Frisian ports, both island and mainland, are all charming in their different ways. Harlingen is one of the most beautiful towns in the area, and the yacht harbour is right in the town, while in Den Helder one is rather a hike from shops and restaurants as there visiting yachts lie in the naval harbour. The island ports are tourist-oriented without being trippery, and do their very best for the visiting yachtsman in spite of overcrowding during the holiday season.

The German islands are quite different in atmosphere. The harbours are far from the towns; wilder and less convenient, but also less crowded. On some, cars are forbidden, and on Wangerooge there is not even a road from the port to the town: one must take a train or walk the three miles along the railway. They take health and quiet very seriously, and taxis are banned from the centres of most towns after 9 p.m. With a very high proportion of visitors, there tend to be many good restaurants, but rather a scarcity of shops, certainly in main streets.

On the German mainland things are again quite different. This is an area of rapid recent development, and while some good yacht harbours have sprung up, they are not yet really used to the idea of visiting yachts. They are not unfriendly, far from it, but they tend to have no visitors' moorings, and indeed there is often no-one who can give advice as to where to go. These are the *siels*: villages or hamlets based on the sluicegates through which flood waters are released through the dyke into the sea. Some are quite large; others, particularly where the dyke has been rebuilt, are almost uninhabited.

But many are well worth a visit, as the reader of the detailed notes will find.

The Jade has somewhat the same atmosphere as the North Sea mainland, and in Hooksiel it has a major and successful yachting centre. Wilhelmshaven is a typical large port, and the Weser has only Bremerhaven, a similar one – comfortable enough when you get there, but I should have thought hardly worth a visit from the average yacht cruising in the area. The Elbe, on the other hand, has several pleasant ports, and is worth visiting in good weather even by yachts who are not intending to go further.

Finally, what can one say about Helgoland? Once under British rule, it is now a unique, schizophrenic place. During the day it is crowded with trippers who arrive in fleets of steamers, mostly with the object of going home with as much low-duty drink as they can manage, both inside and out. At night, however, the population falls sharply and it becomes a charming and relaxed resort.

ROUTES TO THE AREA

For the hard-bitten seagoing reader there will, of course, be no problem, as a direct passage to Den Helder, or even Helgoland, is undoubtedly the quickest way to get to this cruising ground. For those who prefer to avoid long sea passages there is, however, no problem, as once Calais has been reached one can work up the coast in easy stages, with a convenient port never more than a day's sail away. It is an exposed coast, however, particularly north of the Schelde, and indeed the passage from south of the Schelde to Scheveningen, crossing as it does the shipping lanes into Europoort at Hook of Holland, can be troublesome, so it is worth noting that it is quite possible to go by canal from Flushing to Den Helder. Even with a fixed mast this can be done in three days, and a fast motor cruiser might well lower that time. Details of the inland routes will be found in Appendix 5.

The Riddle of the Sands

I cannot end this general introduction without mentioning what is undoubtedly the best book ever written about the area, *The Riddle of the Sands* by Erskine Childers. This brilliant spy thriller is set almost wholly on board a yacht cruising in the Frisian Islands, and although the first few pages are a little dated (it was, after all, written in 1903), once the action moves aboard *Dulcibella* everything could be happening yesterday: in fact it brings home how little yachting has changed in three-quarters of a century – thank goodness! I do urge those lucky ones among my readers who have not already had the pleasure of reading this book to get hold of a copy and take it with them. To read it while cruising the waters in which it is set is a rare pleasure, as I know from experience.

I · Den Helder and the Southwest Waddenzee

Charts: Dutch 1452 or British 191, for approaches from seaward. Also Dutch 1454 with 1456, *or else* Dutch Yacht Chart 1811, for SW Waddenzee

Den Helder

Approaches

As one would expect for the principal naval harbour in Holland, Den Helder is one of the few harbours in this area which can be entered or left in any conditions in which the boat is capable of putting to sea. This is because there are two main channels leading into the Marsdiep (the channel between the mainland and Texel), and if one is impassable it is always possible to go round by the other, which in those circumstances will be sheltered. Coming along the coast from the south, the Schulpengat begins some 4 miles south of the end of the mainland, Kaap Hoofd. The buoyed channel starts about two miles offshore, at buoy SG (Iso 4 sec), and approaches the shore obliquely on a bearing of $026\frac{1}{2}°$ T, marked by leading lights (Front Iso 4 sec, Rear Occ 8 sec) on Texel. The outer buoy also lies on the leading line marked by two lighthouses on the mainland: Grote Kaap (F), and Kleine Kaap (Iso 5 sec), which is used by vessels approaching from the west. Lateral buoyage leads up the channel to an east cardinal buoy S-WG (V Qk Fl (3) 5 sec) where the channel is joined by the smaller Westgat. From here is it safe to shape a course direct for Kaap Hoofd, and proceed from there keeping $\frac{1}{4}$ mile offshore until the harbour entrance opens up.

Coming up the coast in fine weather it is not necessary to go far enough offshore to use the buoyed channel, as the inshore shoal (the Fransche Bankje) carries at least $3\frac{1}{2}$ m. With winds over force 4

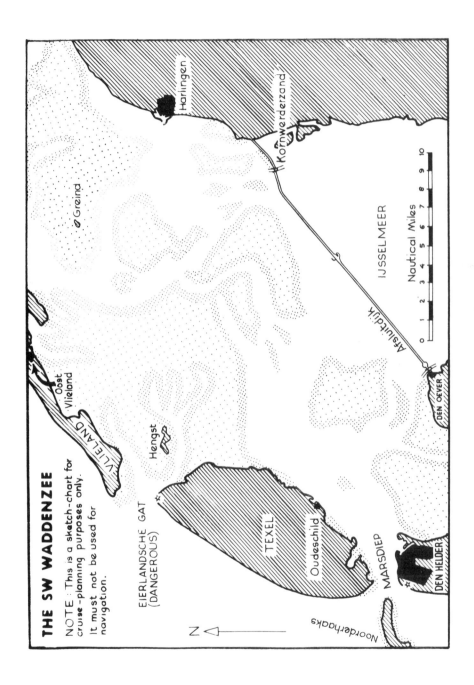

THE SW WADDENZEE

NOTE: This is a sketch-chart for cruise-planning purposes only. It must not be used for navigation.

A perfect landfall! Kaap Hoofd from the SW: Kijkduin light is showing just to port of Huisduinen light.

between south and west, however, the buoyed channel should be used, and even this is dangerous on the ebb with anything over force 6 from the same quarter.

In this case, or when approaching from the north, the Molengat is used. This begins at buoy MG (Iso 8 sec), two miles off the Texel shore and four miles north of the Marsdiep. From here steer 140° until the first port-hand buoy is identified, after which the channel is well marked and presents no problem. There are leading lights to the west of Den Helder, but yachts are advised to concentrate on the channel buoys and keep to the appropriate side of the channel, out of the way of big ships. The Molengat, in its turn, is rough during the ebb in winds from NW to N above force 4, and dangerous over force 6: in these conditions the Schulpengat would be used.

There is also a third channel, the Westgat, which provides a useful short-cut in good weather when approaching from the west. Its entrance buoy (ZH) lies 3 miles WNW of the buoy for the

Schulpengat, and the channel is well marked thereafter by lateral buoyage. It can be very rough indeed, however, in winds above force 4 between SE and W at any state of the tide, so it should only be used in good and settled weather.

Entrance and berthing
Approaching from the west, keeping about ¼ mile offshore, the first basin that will be seen is the ferry harbour. When passing this a close watch must be kept, as the ferries enter and leave at great speed and must be given right of way. Beyond the ferry port a pier 200 m long forms the west side of the main harbour entrance. Once this is rounded, the harbour may be entered. Avoid approaching the pier closer than 100 m, and be sure to pass west of the red buoy north of the east pierhead, as the water is shoal to the east. The tide runs past the harbour entrance at up to 3 knots at high springs, so be prepared to avoid being swept sideways, and watch out for eddies in the

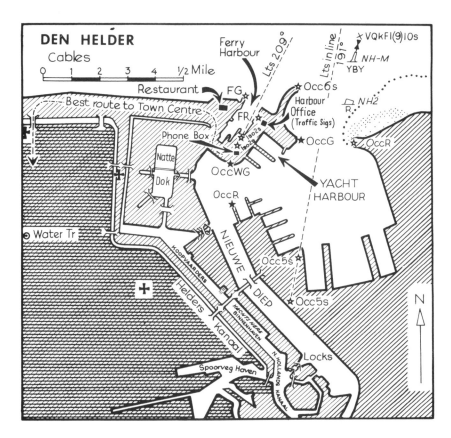

entrance. Signal lights, red over white over red, or white red white horizontally, shown from both sides of the entrance, forbid entry.

Inside, the yacht harbour is the first basin on the starboard side. Moorings are of the kind which will be met in many ports in the area: bows to a pontoon with stern lines to two posts. For readers who have never encountered this method of mooring, the secret is to have one stern warp ready with a bowline at the end and slip it over the upwind post while passing. Then, once a bow warp is made fast to the pontoon, it can be veered and the stern line hauled in until the second stern warp can be put over its post at leisure. Then one can pay out the stern warps until the bow warp can be made fast just short enough to step ashore, after which the stern warps are hauled in and made fast as tight as possible. Most yachts that get into trouble do so because they steer midway between the posts leaving them too far away for either crewman to get his loop in position: leave it to one, and put him amidships, with the warp led outside everything from a stern fairlead. Then he can place his loop over the upwind post with no fuss. If he is stationed on the quarter he may miss, or the boat may have to be slanted to bring him within range, with problems later. Make sure there is enough stern warp, and that it is coiled to run out freely, as to be brought up all-standing out of reach of the pontoon usually ends in fouling your downwind neighbour.

If the harbourmaster has not directed the visitor to a berth, he should apply at the harbour office (see plan) for permission to stay

Den Helder: Royal Navy yacht harbour, seen from the Nieuwe Haven near the entrance. Harbour control and signal tower is right centre; extreme right is the club building, where visitors can use the excellent toilets and showers.

in the chosen berth. Visitors wishing to leave a yacht for several days may prefer to lock into the Koopvaarders Binnenhaven, reached from the Niewediep. This runs south from the west part of the main harbour, and the lock is on the starboard hand after passing through the swing bridge. Lock and bridge are manned from 0500 to 2300 weekdays, and 0700–1300 and 1400–1900 on Sundays. Turn to starboard out of the lock, and the yacht moorings (alongside pontoons) will be seen on the starboard hand. From this harbour also leads the Noordhollands Kanaal, providing a fixed-mast inshore route to Amsterdam and the south, a valuable alternative if the weather is bad.

Facilities

The town is about a mile from the naval yacht harbour. Walk west along the seafront past the ferry harbour and take the second main road on the left. Excellent shopping and restaurants. Frequent railway services make the town a good place to pick up or drop crew. It is a long way to walk for a meal, though, particularly in bad weather, and it is worth knowing that there is a good restaurant at the ferry terminal, only $\frac{1}{4}$ mile from the outer yacht harbour. Diesel from pump near yacht harbour office and water by hose. No petrol except in cans from garages. (Note: petrol is *benzine* in Dutch.)

The tidal yacht harbour is run by the Royal Naval Y.C., a club for naval officers. It is nearby (see plan), and visiting yachtsmen can use the showers and toilets (super), but not the club as this is not only for for yachting members but for all officers. The inner harbour has two clubs, and although the moorings appear continuous they will be found to be divided by a wire fence. The first moorings belong to the Marine Watersportvereniging (a naval petty-officers' club), and the further ones to the private Helder-Willemsoord-Nieuwediep Club, whose clubhouse is under the bridge at the end of the canal. The naval club is open for longer hours and more often, and I would advise it as the better bet. Both clubs have toilets and showers, and water by hose, but the slight advantage in facilities and nearness to town (marginal) hardly seem likely to make it worth the bother to lock in, unless using the canal.

THE SOUTHWEST WADDENZEE

Tides

In the wide SW part of the Waddenzee the tides are both complex and strong, so it is essential to carry the tidal atlas issued by the

Sailing in the Waddenzee.

Dutch Hydrographic Department (available in the UK through Potters). This is called *Stroomatlas Waddenzee, Westelijk deel* and covers the waters from Den Helder to the east end of the island of Ameland. Broadly speaking, in this part of the Waddenzee the flood tide pours in through the entrances towards Harlingen, and the ebb runs back out to sea from there, but there are considerable differences in timing, and when the banks are covered towards high water there are strong cross-sets that can carry the unwary out of the channel and into shoal water. If properly used, however, the streams are most convenient for the yachtsman, and by leaving Den Helder $5\frac{1}{2}$ hours after HW Harlingen, even a slow yacht will carry a fair tide all the 30 miles to Harlingen, and 20 miles further to Terschelling on the ebb if required. It is not everywhere you can do 50 miles with a fair tide all the way! Leaving at the same time and maintaining five knots, it is also possible to run the flood up to the watershed of the Vlakte van Oostbierum and drop down to Ameland on the ebb, with enough water left to anchor in the Ballumerbocht, though probably not enough to get into Nes.

Coming south from Terschelling, the problem is the first 3 miles to the Vliestroom. Bound for Harlingen, a boat that can make five knots against the first foul stream can leave 5 hours before Harlingen HW, but a slower vessel is wiser to make it $5\frac{1}{2}$ hours after the previous HW, to get the benefit of the last of the ebb down to the Vliestroom.

Channels and Passages
East of Den Helder, the wide Marsdiep quickly divides into the main Texelstroom and the smaller Malzwin. The latter would normally only be used if bound for Den Oever and the Ijsselmeer via the Wierbalg, although there is a northern branch, the Zwin, that can be joined through the Visjagersgaatje at buoy W-VG, and leads up to the great Afsluitdijk, past the monument De Vlieter, and on up towards Harlingen, or back to the Texelstroom by the buoyed Vlieter channel.

Most yachts, however, will ride the faster flood up the Texelstroom. About 12 miles from Den Helder it divides at buoy D-SO, into the Scheurrak (SO buoys) leading north towards Terschelling, and the Doove Balg leading east to Harlingen. Using the Scheurrak on passage to Terschelling, you will do better to postpone leaving Den Helder until 5 hours before HW Harlingen to get a fair tide down the Inschot to Terschelling, but beware of fierce streams in the Marsdiep when emerging from the harbour.

The Doove Balg leads back to the Dyke, and divides just before

Kornwerderzand into the Zuidoostrak (cutting through to the In-schot, and providing a short route from Kornwerderzand to Ter-schelling) and the Boontjes, which leads to Harlingen.

From Harlingen the Pollendam keeps open a direct route to Terschelling via the Blauwe Slenk and the Vliestroom. Watch out for very complex buoyage round the entrance to the Schuitengat (which leads to Terschelling) at buoy VL-SG, as the sands here shift constantly and the chart may be misleading. Keep your eyes open and sound! This entrance, and that of Oost Vlieland, are dealt with in the next section, as are the channels to the east.

The Eierlandsche Gat between Texel and Vlieland is dangerous, unmarked, and a military range, and should not be attempted, so the two watt channels running north from the Texelstroom have little value to the yachtsman; and in any case the area is a nature reserve and should be avoided during the breeding season, which is when most visitors are likely to be there.

HARBOURS OF THE SOUTHWEST WADDENZEE

Den Helder (see pages 25–30 above)

Oudeschild
This pleasant harbour lies on the north side of the Texelstroom, some 6 miles NE of Den Helder. Approach is straightforward but

The entrance to Oudeschild. The final approach buoy, OS2, can be seen below and to the right of the windmill.

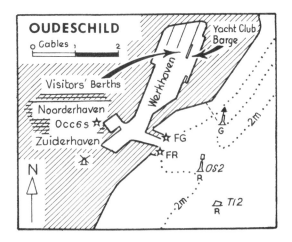

Oudeschild yacht basin. The club barge, white with a flat roof, can be seen behind the yachts.

the entrance requires care, as cross-tides of up to three knots may be met. Make buoy T12, and from there keep on a straight line, checking astern regularly, to buoy OS2, which should be left close to port. Proceed NW until the south pier is well open, when it is safe to enter. The yacht harbour is in the Werkhaven, NNE of the entrance. Berth alongside on the west side of the club barge, or as directed.

The barge has good toilets and showers, and the bar, which provides light meals, is open 0800 to 2400. Water from hose; diesel pump. This harbour is a major new development and the large yacht basin was only dug in the 1970s, so it is not surprising that it is rather expensive. In 1978 rates were Fl.1 per metre, plus a tourist tax of 0.65 per person per visit. But for a new harbour created from nothing this seems to me fair enough.

Den Oever
At the SW end of the Afsluitdijk which closes off the Ijsselmeer, this is a sea-lock with no facilities for yachts. However, it would be possible to shelter there from a sudden W or NW gale, when the Visserhaven would be the best bet, so I include it for completeness.

Kornwerderzand
Like Den Oever, this lock complex can be used for shelter in a real emergency; indeed in 1978 I left Harlingen for Texel in a north-

Kornwerderzand. A harbour of refuge only, unless locking through into the Ijsselmeer. The other yacht actually *was* running for cover.

westerly blow in company with some other Dutch yachts with the same plan, but as we passed Kornwerderzand and it blew up to force 8, they all changed their minds and ran in. (During the next couple of hours, I often wished I had done the same!) There is room in the Voorhaven to secure to a fishing boat and wait out a blow, but yachts would not be encouraged to stay there in good weather, and of course should not be left unattended. No facilities.

Harlingen from the south. The entrance is round the pierhead on
the extreme left of the picture.

Harlingen

This is one of the most important harbours in the southern part of
our area, and also one of the most beautiful. The approach and
entrance are straightforward from any direction, although the
entrance can be very rough near high water in strong winds between
SW and W.

Visitors from seaward do best to enter the Noorderhaven, reached
through the Oude Buitenhaven, just north of the railway quay. Two
bridges have to be passed. On weekdays these are opened at half past
every hour, but only if needed, so make sure you are visible, particularly when wanting to leave. Once through, moor as near as
possible to the next bridge, but do not go through unless instructed,
as there is seldom room in the inner part of the harbour. There were
pontoons for the easternmost 80 m of the outer harbour in 1978: it
was planned to extend them. The harbour has 1.6 m depth at LWS.
Water and electricity on pontoons. Toilets (24 hours) round the back
of Watersport Leeuwenbrug's chandlery at the E end of the harbour:
Leeuwenbrug are also the harbourmasters and charge the moderate
dues. Showers (antique) in the Green Cross building, 21 Noordijs,
open 8–10 a.m. and 5–7 p.m.

Two excellent chandlers and a sailmaker overlook the harbour,

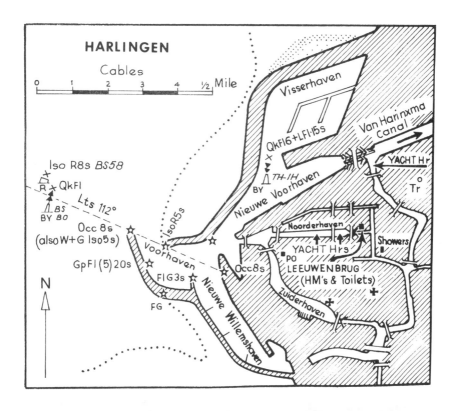

HARLINGEN

Cables

0   1   2   3   4   ½ Mile

Visserhaven

Van Harinxma Canal

QkFl6+LFl·15s

YACHT Hr

Iso R8s *BS58*

R QkFl

Lts 112°

BS
BY *80*

Occ 8s
(also W+G Iso5s)

GpFl(5)20s

N

Voorhaven

Iso R5s

TH-1H
BY

Nieuwe Voorhaven

Occ8s

FlG3s

FG

Nieuwe Willemshaven

Noorderhaven

YACHT Hrs

PO

LEEUWENBRUG
(HM's & Toilets)

Zuiderhaven

Showers

Tr

Harlingen: the Noorderhaven from outside Watersport
Leeuwenbrug.

and all charts, books etc are available. Leeuwenbrug also have a telephone which you can use and pay afterwards, useful if like me you are rendered speechless by the need to stuff coins in a slot every ten seconds! All manner of repairs can be arranged through the same firm.

One useful service available here, and as far as I know nowhere else, is provided by Walinga, Gt. Ossenmarkt 3, on the corner of the Zuiderhaven. This is the refilling of Calor Gas bottles while you wait: no problem with English fittings.

Approaching through or bound for the van Harinxmakanaal (see Appendix 5 on inland waterways), there is another yacht harbour on the south side of the canal *immediately* east of the locks (indeed the entrance is almost hidden by the south wall of the southern lock). The entrance is very narrow, no more than 5 m, and it is rather shallow, with only about 1.3 m on the moorings (bow to jetty, stern to posts). However the bottom is very soft, and boats of slightly greater draft can be pulley-hauleyed into position with a bit of effort. Good toilets and showers in green hut at north end of quay. Water from hose.

Harlingen: the yacht harbour in the van Harinxma Canal. Note the very narrow entrance, visible top centre half hidden behind the wall of the southern lock.

There is no fuel in either yacht harbour, though Leeuwenbrug are trying to arrange supply, but diesel can be had from a barge in the Voorhaven. I found the restaurant *De Gastronoom* in Voorstraat (parallel to the Noorderhaven, one street to the west) to be excellent value, but there are many other good ones. Altogether a most pleasant town with many beautiful old buildings, and well worth a visit. One word of warning: at exceptionally high tides the entire outer yacht harbour is closed off by a flood gate for up to $1\frac{1}{2}$ hours either side of HW.

II · Vlieland to the Lauwersmeer

Charts: Dutch 1454, 1456, 1458; *or* Dutch Yacht Charts 1811, 1812

THE ZEEGATS

The Zeegat van Terschelling is one of the better possibilities on this coast in bad weather, and in fact I would say that a seaworthy yacht would always manage to get in, though it would be impossible to leave in gales from W to NW. The main channel is the Zuider Stortemelk, approached from buoy VSM about 3 miles off the Vlieland shore. The channel is deep and well lit, and on the flood there is never too much sea, although in easterly gales it would be wiser to use the Thomas Smit Gat. For the Zuider Stortemelk follow the well-lit channel to buoy ZS-VS, and then continue round for Vlieland or steer about 60° M for Terschelling. The Stortemelk channel lies just to the north, and goes direct to the entrance of Terschelling harbour, but the buoys are not lit and the water is shallower, so it should only be used in good visibility and reasonable weather. It is approached from the same outer buoy (VSM).

The Thomas Smit Gat is used when approaching from the east, or in strong winds from between E and S. It is sheltered from these quarters, but can be unpleasant in even moderate NW winds, especially on the ebb.

The Zeegat van Ameland lies between Terschelling and Ameland, and the only buoyed channel is the Westgat. It is safe except in strong onshore winds, and is the easiest of the zeegats to enter in bad visibility, as the 3 m line north of Terschelling is steep-to and can safely be followed on soundings until it leads SE into the Borndiep. The Westgat is approached from buoy VWG: in calm weather and with good visibility it is possible at half tide to cut across the Born-

VLIELAND TO THE LAUWERSMEER

NOTE: This is a sketch-chart for cruise-planning purposes only. It must not be used for navigation.

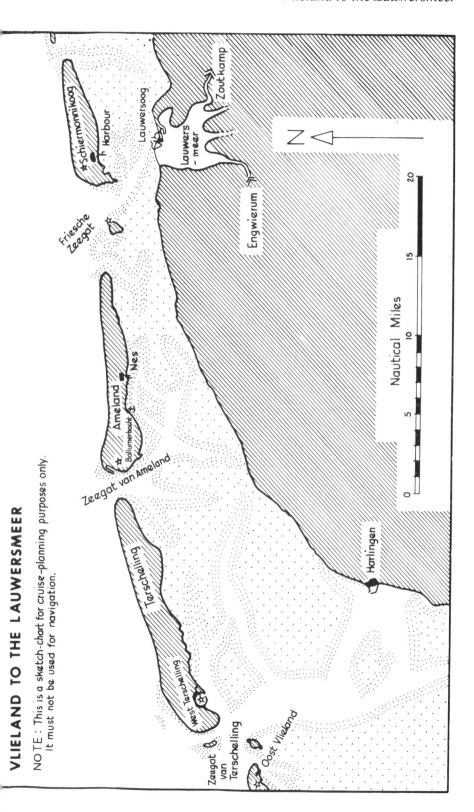

Schiermonnikoog

Harbour

Lauwersoog

Zoutkamp

Lauwers-meer

Friesche Zeegat

Engwierum

N

Ameland

Nes

Ballumerbocht

Zeegat van Ameland

Terschelling

West Terschelling

Zeegat van Terschelling

Oost Vlieland

Harlingen

Nautical Miles

0   5   10   15   20

riff by steering just W of S from buoy BR to the west cardinal buoy to the south, and then via a yellow conical buoy into the main channel. This saves about 5 miles when coming from the east, but should only be attempted in good weather. Minimum depth 2.5 m at half tide.

Finally, the Friesche Zeegat lies between Ameland and Schiermonnikoog. Here again, the only buoyed channel is called the Westgat, approached from buoy VWG. The channel is well buoyed and lit. Coming from the west, in really good visibility, two yellow can buoys A and B mark a safe line of approach some $1\frac{1}{2}$ miles south of the main channel, and from the east the Plaatgat can be found by careful sounding along the 1 m line (having, of course, added the height of tide to the 1 m!), but the latter can only be used in calm weather and above half tide. It is, however, safe to approach the Westgat on a transit between buoys WG5 and WG6 from the north, as long as they can be positively identified, and coming from the east this saves over 3 miles compared with going round by VWG. This gat is dangerous on the ebb in strong winds between W and N.

I should perhaps end this section by explaining why I said that one can get in, but not out of, Terschelling in such conditions. All these zeegats suffer from more or less dangerous seas when an onshore

Oost Vlieland: the harbour entrance. A red flag or two red lights on the pier warns that the harbour is closed by a chain across the entrance.

wind blows over the ebb tide. In such conditions one can neither get in nor out safely. However, the yacht at sea can wait till the flood begins. This makes the seas far less dangerous, and then there should be no danger at sufficient rise of tide and with a seaworthy boat. But of course the boat wishing to get out is still stuck, because with a strong wind and tide both against him, he will be unable to make any headway. Entering the first two gats above may be attempted in onshore winds once the flood is well established: the Friesche Zeegat is best left until half tide in such conditions.

VLIELAND, TERSCHELLING AND PASSAGES TO THE EAST

Vlieland is unique in having its town and harbour near the east end of the island, and so it and Terschelling are the only two island harbours that share the same zeegat.

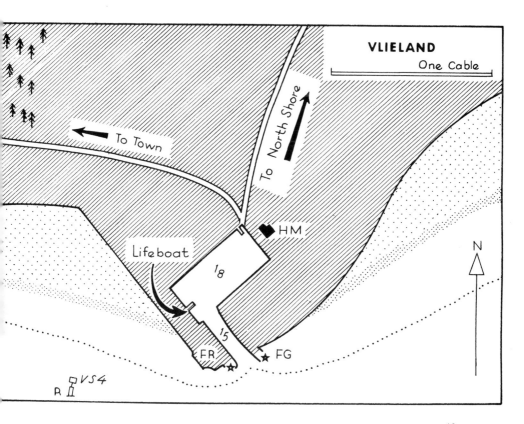

Vlieland

Major works for the extension of this harbour began in late 1978, and as a result it will be closed to yachts except as a harbour of refuge in emergencies throughout 1979, and probably 1980 as well. However, when the works are completed there will be a new yacht basin separate from the fishing harbour, and it will become one of the most important yacht harbours in the area, as the island is very beautiful.

The entrance through the Vliesloot is easy and well buoyed, but it is worth noting that, from the south, there is an alternative HW entrance via the Fransche Gaatje and the Vlielander Balg. It is some years since I sailed this channel, but I believe the depths are more or less what I found in 1970, which was 1.3 m at HW on a neap tide. The advantage of the channel is in a gale between W and NW, when the normal Vliesloot approach leads through totally exposed waters. The overland route is completely sheltered, and one can lie comfortably at anchor in the Gaatje and wait for enough tide to slip over to Vlieland. If using this route, do not turn W before rounding buoy VB2, as the shoal extends almost to the mark.

In the meantime, if one wishes to visit the island, one can anchor off the village about 150 m west of the ferry pier in about 1½ m at LW, and land by dinghy. However, this anchorage is dangerous in strong S to SW winds, and should on no account be used if there is any risk that they might develop.

The interior of Vlieland harbour.

Terschelling

The harbour is approached via the Schuitengat from buoy VL-SG. The channel is narrow and shifts, but as long as the buoys are followed carefully there is no difficulty. Yachts moor at the north end of the usually crowded harbour, and it can be difficult to find a satisfactory berth during the holiday season. Berths are exposed and uncomfortable near HW in strong E winds. Try to arrive early if visiting in the high season, as otherwise an uncomfortable night can ensue!

The great advantage of Terschelling is that the harbour is in the town, which makes it far more convenient for provisioning than any of the other Island ports, and indeed I have used it as a departure point for Norway for this reason. Water, however, can only be had in cans, though diesel can be got from a truck by arrangement with the harbourmaster.

There is considerable commercial traffic in and out of the harbour, and strong cross-tides may be met in the entrance, so approach the pierheads only when the entrance is open and be prepared for eddies. At night approach along the west sector of the main light, which provides a safe path avoiding unlit buoys.

The town is a pleasant one, with good shops and restaurants, but rather trippery compared with Vlieland. It has the fine old Brandaris light-tower, but few other old buildings, perhaps because the English burnt it to the ground in 1666.

West Terschelling: harbour entrance from the SE.

The yacht harbour at Terschelling comes into view only when
well in between the piers.

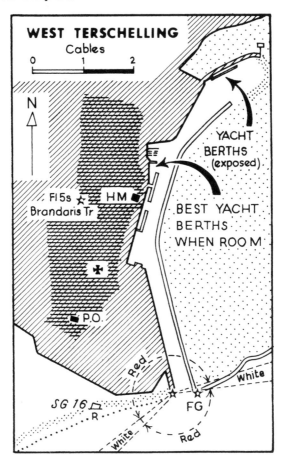

The watt-passages to the east

From Harlingen, the well buoyed Vlakte van Oostbierum runs for about 10 miles NE along the coast to the Vaarwater van de Zwarte Haan (Channel of the Black Hen). As the buoyage is now in the direction of the main flood stream, all the green buoys which mark the channel are left to starboard when one is going NE. From here a choice of two well marked channels leads to the Borndiep and Ameland. There are two watersheds close together, one around VO-29 and one near VH6. (By now red buoys appear, which are left to port on the NE course.) The first is about 1.6 m deep at HW neaps, and the second 1.8 m, with about 0.3 m more depth in each case at springs. This is one of the shallower passages; aim to leave Harlingen 3 hours before HW there, which will bring you to the watershed an hour or so before HW, with a few centimetres of rising tide still to go. The pilotage is simple: after NOM-VO make sure the next buoy you make is VO-7 (green) and then the VO series is simply followed to VO-45. Then comes VH-VO, and then the VH series beginning with red buoys 2, 4 and 6, and continuing mostly red to VH-28 and KB-VH. After that, the VH continuation provides the slightly shorter route to Nes.

The northern watt-passage is rather deeper. From the entrance of Terschelling one can turn straight to the E and follow the O buoys (Oosterom), but from Vlieland it is quicker to use the West and Noord Meeps and Noorder Balgen: the routes join at NB3. Follow on the O series, and the watershed will be passed at around O-32. There is about 1.9 m at HW neaps, and 2.2 m at HW springs. HW at the watershed is about 30 minutes after Harlingen, so I would leave Terschelling about $2\frac{1}{2}$ hours before HW Harlingen, or Vlieland about $3\frac{1}{2}$ hours before, in each case reaching the watershed about an hour before its HW. Once over, the O series continues, again leaving red buoys to port in this direction, to O-68 and WG-O in the Borndiep. From here a SE course leads down the buoyed channel to DG-MG (west cardinal) from where the Molengat leads to the Ballumerbocht and Nes, the alternative berths for Ameland.

AMELAND AND THE PASSAGES TO THE EAST

Ameland has no proper yacht harbour, and visitors must be prepared to take the ground if the tides are anywhere near springs. The entrance from the sea was dealt with on page 40–2; from there or the overland passages, the approach to both stopping places is from between the west cardinal buoys DG-MG and MG4. A NE course from here, leaving the red MG buoys to port, leads up the Molengat. Shortly after MG1, the first starboard-hand buoy, is reached, a light beacon (Iso Red 4 sec) marks the end of a ruined mole running out from the island. Behind this lies the Ballumer-bocht, a creek where about $\frac{1}{2}$ m will be found 100 m from the Ameland shore. This is sheltered from all winds except from E to S, as there is enough mole left to break the seas from S or SW. Supplies from Ballum, a good mile from the landing place.

A mile or so further east lies buoy MG-VG marking the entrance to the ferry port of Nes. The channel is well marked by withies and besoms as far as the end of the new pier, where there is a light (Iso 6 sec) at the end. Yachts must pass round the east side of this and steer N for the old pier, where they may lie with the permission of the Rijkswaterstaat. There is about $1\frac{1}{2}$ m at half tide. The new pier is forbidden for yachts. Supplies from Nes, $\frac{3}{4}$ mile to the north.

The routes eastward to Lauwersoog are long and shallow, as at least two watersheds have to be passed. From Nes or the Ballumerbocht the simplest is the northern route, through the Veerbootgat into the Kikkertgat, which is left at buoy KG-ZSA, to follow the Zuiderspruit Ameland. The ZSA series gives way to withies, and after a watershed with about 1.7 m depth at HW neaps (2.0 m at HW springs) buoy HB-ZSA leads into the Holwerdbalg. From here one proceeds NE to buoy HB-FW, where one can turn southwards into the Friesche Wad, joining the southern route. With too little tide, or deep draft, one may follow the HB series NE to buoy HB-PG, and then SE down the Pinkegat to PG-SG, where a sharp turn NNE leads down the deep Smeriggat into the Zoutkam-perlaag, the main channel to Lauwersoog. The buoys must be followed closely: the 1978 chart here is most confusing as it is one of the occasions where the buoys are printed so as to appear to lead over shoal water. In fact there is a shoal patch between the Pinkegat and the Smeriggat, but it should have at least $1\frac{1}{2}$ m over it at half tide.

The southern route is more likely to be useful after a night at anchor in the open, perhaps in the Zwarte Haan channel after coming up from Harlingen in the evening. The Dantziggat (DG buoys) leads down to the mainland coast, past the long ferry pier at Holwerd (no yachts). From here, a light beacon to the ENE marks the way: leave this to starboard, and continue into the withy channel, running more or less parallel with the coast. It is joined from the north first by the Friesche Wad and then by the Smeriggat, and finally runs out through the Pesensrede (PR buoys) into the Zoutkamperlaag. There is a little more water in this channel, perhaps 1.8 to 2.1 m at HW neaps and springs, but there is almost 7 miles of shallow water to cross so tides must be accurately judged. I would aim to reach the end of the Holwerd pier between 2 and 1 hours before HW Lauwersoog.

SCHIERMONNIKOOG AND LAUWERSOOG

Once in the Zoutkamperlaag, one has the choice of Schiermonnikoog to the north, or Lauwersoog or the Lauwersmeer ports to the south.

Schiermonnikoog
This harbour is built on the old ferry pier, now replaced by a deeper one a mile to the east. The approach channel is narrow and tortuous, and no more than 1.5 m deep at HW on an average tide, with a decimetre or so more or less at springs and neaps. The harbour has a natural sill, and the moorings inside retain between 1.0 and 1.5 m, so if you can get there you are probably all right to stay: keelboats are said to sink into the mud in any case. Harbour dues are among the highest in Holland, but it is a charming place, only a mile from the town, and with showers, toilets etc. From the west the harbour is

Schiermonnikoog: the yacht harbour entrance, with a typical damaged withy that could be of either kind. The island was covered by mist, but the extraordinary 'basketwork' construction of the harbour can be seen.

approached through the Gat van Scheirmonnikoog (GvS buoys), turning N from GvS-5 for R1. After this besoms are left to starboard and withies to port. Bare poles are either withies with no branches (leave to port) or besoms with the heads fallen off (leave to starboard). Keep the echo sounder running while you guess! The entrance is very narrow (15 m): moor as directed when inside, bow and posts. Water by hose, no fuel. In holiday times there is often absolutely no room, so aim to be there by HW to allow time to get out again and run to Lauwersoog, or ring the harbourmaster to reserve a berth (tel. (05195) 544, May–Sept only). The island, whose name 'the Island of the Grey Monks' refers to a monastic settlement that was followed by a period of effective independence in the seventeenth century, is one of the most beautiful of all the Frisians, and is well worth a visit in a suitable yacht.

Between Schiermonnikoog and Lauwersoog there is a useful short-cut in the form of the Geul van Brakzand. This watt-passage carries about 1.9 m at HW neaps (2.3 m at HW springs) and is well marked. The north end lies 4 cables (0.4 nautical miles) east of the GvS-5 buoy, and one should pass east of green BZ buoys and west of withies. The whole of this area is crowded with yellow buoys marking gas pipeline, which have no navigational significance: do not rely on their charted positions, as a later shift in the channel, and thus the channel buoys, can render this misleading.

Lauwersoog
I seem fated always to visit this harbour in terrible weather, but at least that enables me to say with confidence that it provides good shelter in all conditions. It is possible to spend a night in the outer harbour alongside a fishing boat in the Visserhaven, but this can be uncomfortable, with swell in bad weather, and always wash from manoeuvring ships. Unless there are special reasons, better to lock into the Lauwersmeer: the locks operate 0400–2100 weekdays, 0400–1800 Saturdays, and 0900–1000 and 1630–1830 Sundays: no charge. Look out for a strong stream in the lock: I have known it run as fast as 2 knots outwards. A warning is shown when this occurs, but as it is a small sign on a piece of wood it is not always easy to see from the outside. Once through the lock into the Lauwersmeer the yacht harbour lies to the SE; it is safe to keep close along the shore until the harbour opens up. Visitors' moorings are on the near side of the first pontoon, or as directed. Water on pontoons, diesel from pump. Petrol from near the ferry terminal in the outer harbour. Showers and toilets are in the brown building at the SE corner of the yacht harbour. Modest dues. Small self-service store and good

Lauwersoog: the seaward entrance from the Zoutkamperlaag.
The sluices are visible to the right, and the masts of ships show
the Vissershaven to the left of picture. The lock leads into the
Lauwersmeer and inner harbour.

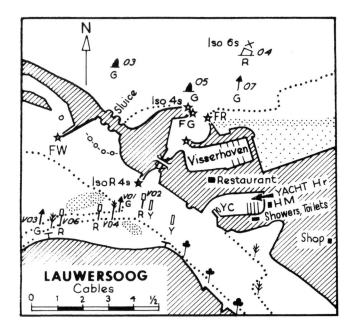

Lauwersoog: the yacht harbour in the Lauwersmeer. A yacht is entering from the right; the club barge is at right centre, with a flat roof and flag flying.

restaurant at the campsite 250 m to the east. The nice yacht club on a barge is open weekends, and every day in the holiday season; it lies at the west end of the harbour. Apart from a restaurant on the dyke and a few industrial buildings, there is really no town here – the locks are in what was open sea until a few years ago – but it is a comfortable place to lie, and everything that is needed is available. Alternatively there is a charming yacht harbour at Oostmahorn, 2 miles south across the Lauwersmeer. This lake gives communication by canal with Harlingen and the Ijsselmeer (via Engwierum), and with Groningen and Delfzijl via Zoutkamp and the Reitdiep. A chart of the lake appears on Dutch Yacht Chart 1812, and if Born's canal map is carried aboard one can manage to find one's way through the canal system, which can be most useful if the weather turns nasty.

III · Lauwersoog to the Ems and the German Islands

Charts: Dutch Yacht Chart 1812, *or* a choice between Dutch 1460 with 1555, *or* German 90 with 91; in addition, German 89 for the waters east of the Ems

LAUWERSOOG TO BORKUM

The inshore route from Lauwersoog to Borkum is too long for any but a shallow draft vessel to make on one tide, unless the water level is raised by W or NW winds. However it is still very useful as there are sheltered anchorages where a tide can be waited out, or one can run down one of the channels that lead out to sea and cut into the Hubertgat, and so to the island of Borkum and the Ems. I have in fact twice made Borkum to Lauwersoog on a tide, with 1.20 m draft and motoring at $5\frac{1}{2}$–6 knots, but both times I had to cut every possible corner, and still bounced over the last watershed.

The route east from Lauwersoog begins up the Oort channel (O buoys) which lead to a withy channel and the first, and shallowest, watershed over the Lutjewad. Here there is about 2 m depth at HW neaps (2.2 m at HW springs), but it is difficult to be precise as the bottom is soft mud and varies from day to day. (It is possible to plough through it for a considerable distance under power.) After the withies, which as usual mark the north side of the channel, buoy EB-LW offers the first chance of running down to the sea by the buoyed Eilanderbalg. This is a tricky channel at the seaward end, however, and I would not recommend it. Turning SE, buoys EB4 and EB2 lead to another watt-channel over the Hornhuizerwad to the Spuit (SP buoys). This carries about 2.1 m at HW neaps.

The Spuit can be followed by a well buoyed deep-water channel into the Lauwers channel, and so into the open sea, where one may

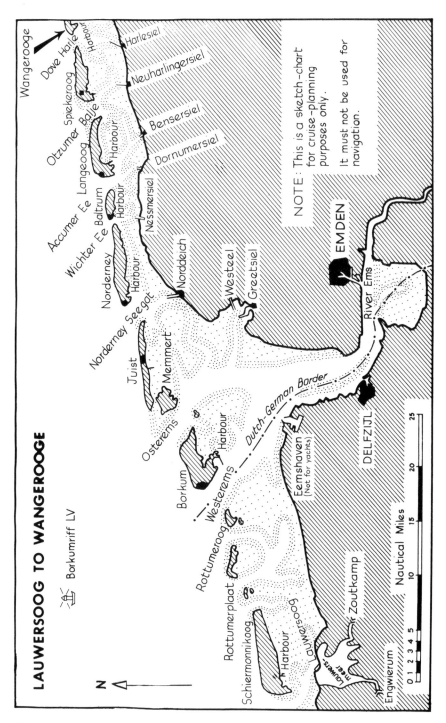

LAUWERSOOG TO WANGEROOGE

NOTE: This is a sketch-chart for cruise-planning purposes only.

It must not be used for navigation.

cut north into the Hubertgat for Borkum from not less than 1 mile west of buoy L2. At first sight the route down the Spuit and up the Hubertgat looks like the quickest way to Borkum, but the snag is that the ebb will be well established by the time the Hubertgat is reached, and the stream runs very strongly, so the 14 miles to the entrance of Borkum is a long, slow slog.

It is quicker, if time and tide allow, to turn SE at SP-PW, cross the short watt-passage over the Pieterburen Wad to the Robbengat (RG buoys), and then turn E up the Zuid-Oost Lauwers (ZOL buoys). This leads over a last long watt to a light beacon marking the end of the Ra (R-series buoys) and so into the Westerems. Here the ebb will run one quickly down to the entrance to Borkum. The Pieterburen passage carries about 2.1 m at HW neaps, and the last one is a little deeper: perhaps 2.2 m, with 0.2 m more at springs in both cases. I would say that the draft limit to achieve the crossing on one tide, on an average tide with no strong wind effect, would be 1.5 m going east and 1.3 m going west. The difference is due to HW Borkum being about an hour after HW Lauwersoog, but going east one must be at the first watershed at least two hours before HW, and plough through as soon as possible to take full advantage of the effect. Tidal streams are not strong, but the Z-O Lauwers can be very rough in strong NW winds, when only powerful vessels should attempt the westbound passage.

For reasons explained above, the offshore route via the Lauwers is unsatisfactory, as it involves a long plug against a rapid ebb. Much quicker is to begin by 'wasting' about 5 miles travelling west along the Zoutkamperlaag. This then turns north, and passing out of the Westgat (page 42) one then has a straight run up to the entrance of the Hubertgat. The transit on buoys WG5 and WG6 can be used in good weather (but keep the depth sounder going, as it is always possible that they may be shifted in the future), and the great joy of this route is that a strong fair tide can be carried most of the way. Leaving Lauwersoog about $3\frac{1}{2}$ hours after HW there, the ebb carries you quickly down to the Westgat. By the time you have reached a position a mile north of WG6, and can safely shape course for the Hubertgat buoy, the main west-going stream will have lost most of its force, and within an hour or two the new flood will begin running up the Ems, carrying you on its way. Once in the Hubertgat there are no problems as far as Borkum: it is well buoyed, and has in addition two light beacons (both Gp Fl (5) 20 sec) just south of the channel, 12 and 4 miles west of Borkum entrance.

Borkum: the Fischerbalje light beacon (left). The Leitdamm can be seen just awash to its right, and the Fischerbalje buoy in the foreground.

Borkum

Arriving from any direction, the Fischerbalje beacon (Gp Occ (2) 16 sec) must be identified. To the west of the beacon at a distance of about 200 m lies the Leitdamm W buoy (west cardinal). This marks a sunken extension of the Leitdamm (training wall) so on no account try to pass between it and the beacon. On approach, the large green Fischerbalje buoy will be seen (Int Qk Fl 13 sec). At low tide one may also see the line of the Leitdamm that forms the northern side of the channel up to the harbour, but this covers at HW. The channel is well buoyed, *but beware strong cross-currents in the entrance and for the first 250 m of the channel.* The main stream up and down the Ems can run at up to 3 knots, and near HW there are extra complications as the banks and dam are covered, but as long as a close eye is kept on the tidal sets there is no problem, although I would not advise trying to enter under sail, particularly in light airs.

Once in the Fischerbalje channel there is no further problem. The harbour is the first opening on the port hand. The second pontoon from the entrance is reserved for yachts during the season: berth there if possible, otherwise where space allows and check with the harbour office. The harbour listens on VHF channel 16. Water on the yacht pontoon, but as it is from a short hose it is necessary to berth fairly near the root of the pontoon to take on water. Diesel from the Shell station at the south end of the harbour: it is not

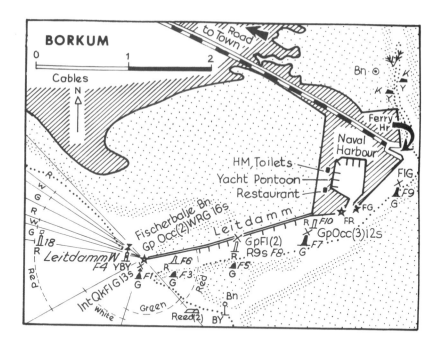

Borkum harbour, interior.

always manned, but the harbourmaster will telephone to arrange delivery (they do not fancy coming out from town for small (50 L?) amounts). Petrol is not available in the harbour.

There are showers and toilets at the harbour office, and a restaurant overlooking the harbour is open all day in the high season, and sporadically at other times. An Italian restaurant will be found a mile along the road towards the town.

The town itself is 7 km from the harbour, but the energetic who try the walk will be deceived by the first buildings into thinking it nearer: Borkum town has outskirts verging on suburbs! Many good restaurants and hotels, but rather disappointing food shops. There is an infrequent bus service to and from the town.

The harbourmaster is a splendid character, and does all he can to be friendly and helpful to visiting yachtsmen, as do his staff and his son, a local lifeboatman. The harbour, however, is less sheltered than appears from the chart, and it can be a restless berth in bad weather. But it is a most important staging point on passage, and I hope that the facilities for yachts may one day be improved, as a fairly small additional expense would enable many more berths to be provided.

THE EMS: ESTUARY AND RIVER TO EMDEN

The Ems divides into two main channels near its mouth, the Westerems, partially covered in the previous section, and the Osterems, which runs east and north of Borkum to the sea. Both are highly important yachting thoroughfares.

The Westerems itself divides just west of Borkum into the Hubertgat, described above, and the Westerems, which runs out 2 or 3 miles further north. The latter is mainly useful as a route between Borkum and the east. From the red buoy Riffgat 6 it is safe to turn north, keeping back-bearings to insure against being set to the east, and cut over the Hohes Riff into the Osterems, from where the route eastward is open. There is at least $3\frac{1}{2}$ m at LW springs on this route, and it is safe except in W to N winds above force 5, when it becomes dangerously rough on the ebb. The main Westerems is buoyed for another 7 miles to the west, but I can see little reason for a west-bound yacht ever to use it rather than the Hubertgat, except if beginning a direct passage to England.

The Osterems provides a link between the upper river and the channels to Norderney and the east, and also a quick way out to sea and the west from Greetsiel and, by way of the watt, from further east. The southern part carries rather less than a metre of water at LW springs, but this channel is well sheltered and I have never known it rough, though it looks as though it might be in strong N or S winds against the tide. The channel is buoyed, but the buoys are small and in moderate visibility I have found it quite tricky to follow, although north of O-34 the tide runs straight up and down the channel. The outer part of the estuary north of the junction with the Ley and Bants Balje is well marked, and there is no difficulty in following it out into open sea. If going east, it is safe to turn north from O-6, and bear away east after $1\frac{1}{2}$ miles. The buoyed channel bends north to keep east of the Kachelotplate shoal, but when bound west in good weather I have often left the buoyed channel at O-17 and steered to pass close north of Borkum. From close off the northernmost point of the island, a course of 280° M leads safely north of the Hohes Riff and out through the old mouth of the river. There is, however, a 4 m bar across this passage, and it would be most unwise to attempt it against fresh or stronger W or NW winds.

A short-cut between the Westerems and Osterems is provided by the Borkum Watt. Marked by withies, this channel runs north from Borkum ferry harbour for about a mile, and then turns NE until it passes close under Hohe Hörn, the easternmost point of the island, after which two red can buoys F12 and F14 lead into the Osterems. The NE part of the channel is also known as Hörns Balje.

Unfortunately it is one of the shallower watt-passages, with about 1.4 m at HW neaps and 1.7 at HW springs, so it is of less value as a route to or from the inshore waters to the east, e.g. Greetsiel, because the distance between its watershed, which can only be crossed near HW, and the other watershed or shallow channel involved, is so great. On a spring tide, however, it is often possible to combine it with the Memmert Balje (page 68) to provide a short route between Borkum and Norderney, as the Memmert channel carries 2.0 m at HW: so with 11 miles between the watersheds it is possible to cross both with a draft under 1.4 m, as long as the first watershed is scraped over as soon as the rising tide allows.

The main value of the Borkumer Wattfahrwasser (to give it its full name) is, however, as a short-cut when leaving Borkum for the east, as it saves several miles compared with leaving by the Westerems and circling the Hohes Riff.

Proceeding up the Westerems from Borkum, the only possible difficulty is an excess of information, especially at night. The river can look rather like Piccadilly, with the added complication that almost all the fixed lights are sectored, and keep changing their characteristics just as you are trying to identify them! But it is a good fault, and one can always approach a buoy close enough to read its numbers if in doubt. The channel divides at buoy DG-BW, and for Delfzijl it is necessary to keep to the Bocht van Watum, which lies west of the Hundsteert sand. This narrow but well marked channel leads past Delfzijl and rejoins the main river at buoy PS-BW.

Delfzijl

One of the most important harbours in the area, which offers sheltered and comfortable accommodation, excellent shopping facilities close to the harbour, and is the headquarters of one of the leading Dutch chart agents and chandlers in the firm of Datema

Delfzijl, showing recent and planned alterations to the harbour. All vessels must now use the SE entrance indicated and proceed down the main fairway. The entrance to the Old Eemskanaal is in the lower right corner of the picture, and the large new Eemskanaal locks are at right centre.

(pronounced 'Dart-Emma') at 11 Oude Schans. It also gives access by canal to the south of Holland (see Appendix 5), and indeed it is quite possible for a yacht with a fixed mast to go all the way from here to Flushing, by canal except for a crossing of the Ijsselmeer, in five days.

Until late in 1978, the entrance to Delfzijl was at the west end of the harbour, but this has now been dammed off and the only entrance which remains is at the east end of the Zeehavenkanaal, some 3 miles ESE of the main lighthouse and the old entrance. The entrance is between two pierheads, Qk Fl Green to starboard (on the west side) and F Red to port. Allow for cross-tides when approaching: these can be very strong at times.

It is nearly 3 miles from the entrance to the main part of the harbour. The channel is well marked by light beacons, Qk Fl Green on the starboard (N) side and Fl or Gp Fl Red to port. In 1979 the yacht harbour remains at the NW end of the harbour, as shown on

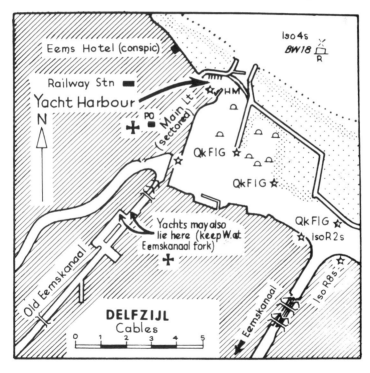

Since this plan was prepared the old entrance has been dammed off as shown. Only the SE entrance near Oterdum is now available, as shown on the photograph. From 1980 the main tidal yacht harbour will be in the enclosure about 3 cables SE of the present one.

the plan, with pontoon berths. Water and diesel at a special fuelling berth. From the 1980 season, yachts will moor in more spacious quarters in the area to the north of the last two starboard-hand beacons coming in from seaward, about 500 m SE of the present yacht harbour. Fuel and water will certainly be available, but the position will be less convenient in that the moorings will be the best part of a mile from town.

Delfzijl is also a good place to leave a yacht, perhaps at the end of a holiday with the idea of bringing it back later over a long weekend. However, cover all winches and other deck equipment, as fine sand and cement dust blows everywhere, and after a couple of weeks berthed there, my winches really did sound like coffee-grinders!

East of Delfzijl, the main channel hugs the northern shore as far as Emden, with a minor branch curling off southwards into the large bay of Dollard. The buoys (with numbers only) are about a half mile apart, and outside them on both sides are numerous north and south cardinal buoys marking the ends of groynes which run south out from the shore, and north from a Leitdamm along the north side of the sandbank opposite.

Emden

Emden is the major German harbour in the region near the Dutch border, but it is not a major yacht centre, and there seems little reason for a yacht with a fixed mast to wish to make a long detour to visit it. Motor cruisers, or yachts with lowering masts, may well find it useful, as it gives access to the Ems-Jade Canal, a good jumping-off point for the Elbe and the Kiel Canal.

Enter between the pierheads, and keep parallel with the west (port-hand) wall which leads up to the Aussenhafen. The small yacht harbour lies at the north end of this, on the east side. Moorings are bows to pier, stern to posts: when manoeuvring allow for the stream which runs through the harbour. Water available. The yacht harbour tends to be deserted at night, as I found to my distress in 1978 when bringing *Kuri Moana* in singlehanded.

The town, with all facilities, is a long way from the berths: over a mile to the centre. There are, however, small restaurants and shops just west of the lock at the north end of the Aussenhafen. Diesel can be had from a barge, petrol only from garages. If there is no berth in the yacht harbour it is necessary to lock in and proceed to yacht moorings in the Jarsummerhafen, at the east end of the southern-most basin. The lock operates 0600–2200, Sundays 0800–1200; signal **NV** in Morse (–· ·· ·–). The outer harbour is uncomfortable in strong SW winds, particularly near HW.

Approaching Emden.

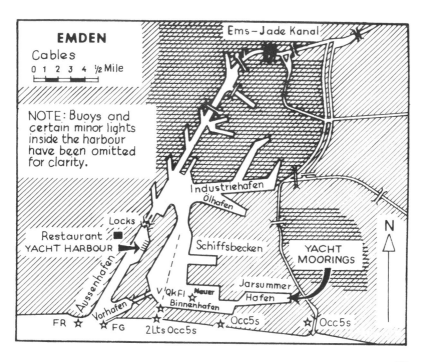

Emden, looking up the Aussenhaven.

Emden: the yacht harbour in the Aussenhaven. Look out for a strong stream through the moorings.

THE EMS TO JUIST, NORDDEICH AND NORDERNEY

The main route eastward from the Ems begins in the Osterems, and the first part was dealt with above. Starting from Delfzijl, the tidal considerations are rather complex. At neaps, the average yacht can get over the shallows in the southern Osterems near LW, and this is the best thing to do. Leaving Delfzijl about 3 hours after HW, the ebb is favourable all the way down the Osterems, and the new flood will then help on the way up Bants Balje to the watershed. It may be necessary to waste an hour to have enough water to cross over, but the tide will be fair nearly all the way. At spring tides, however, the problem is greater. Yachts of any draft will not get over the Osterems shallows for at least 1 hour either side of LW, and if too late there is then a very fast foul stream which has to be fought for about 7 miles. This can slow one so badly that the tide is again foul before the watershed, making a very slow and tiresome passage. I find the best solution at springs is to leave Delfzijl 2 hours after HW. This gives plenty of time to get over the shallows, and although the ebb has to be punched for an hour or so on the way up Bants Balje, the worst is already over and the rate soon begins to slacken. One then anchors for a couple of hours in the Slapersbucht, timing departure to reach the watershed at HW and have the ebb to help on the way down to Norderney, or leaving an hour earlier if going to Norddeich, where this consideration does not arise.

If you *do* miss the tide at a spring and have to plug north against the flood, there is one compensation, which is that it is then safe to cut east from buoy O 24 to L7, and then continue east on to Bb3. At LW, however, one must go on down the Osterems to O 20/Ley 1, and then turn SE for L3. This is the Ley channel, and leads to the charming harbour of Greetsiel, which is well worth a visit even though it is off the beaten track. Continue SSE up the well buoyed channel (L buoys) to the head of the long dyke that runs out into the bay from north of Greetsiel, and will one day sadly be continued to the far shore. Here the channel divides: take the starboard branch, which leads to Greetsiel. There is 2 m of water in the channel for 2 hours either side of HW.

Greetsiel
The main difficulty with the entrance is in the last part of the channel, after the withies which mark the northern part have stopped. The trouble is that at HW springs the marshes on the port side cover completely, so nothing can be seen on that side. Keep fairly close to the starboard shore, depth sounding to warn against getting *too* far in, and all will be well.

At the entrance to the harbour keep to starboard of the headland which faces you and berth in the yacht harbour (on finger pontoons) or as space allows. The harbour dries completely, but the bottom is of mud so soft that even *Kuri Moana*, a bilge-keeler with thick-section keels, sinks into it right down to her normal waterline. This also means that a yacht can be moved with warps into a berth even when there is not really enough water to float her.

There are no facilities apart from a water tap behind the fishing

Greetsiel yacht harbour and entrance near low water. The dredger in mid-channel (at far right of the photo) must be passed close to. Apologies for the 'tornadoes', which are a fault on the negative.

Greetsiel yacht harbour at low water. Boats sink almost to their normal marks in the soft mud.

boat berths, but the town is old and quite charming, with excellent shops and restaurants: it was here that most of the location filming for *The Riddle of the Sands* was done. There is a welcoming feeling about the port and town which is not the case, alas, with all the ports on this coast: do fit in a visit if time allows.

Before returning to the main channels to the east, there is one small watt-passage which can be useful to visitors to Greetsiel: the Greetsieler Legde. This leads across the Hamburger Sand from the Ley channel some 4 miles from Greetsiel, to Bants Balje, the main channel between the Ems and Norderney or Norddeich. It saves about 6 miles between Greetsiel and the east. The channel has just over 2 m at HW neaps, and 2.3 m at HW springs; the withies are laid on the east side of the channel (a fact not at all clear from the Dutch chart, but obvious from German chart 89), and should therefore be left to starboard going north.

We have already followed the route down the Osterems, and across to L3 at low water. Going east, this channel is followed to L4, which is also the Bants Balje buoy. From here a course of about 160° M leads to Bb2, after which the channel is closely marked. If the short-cut to L7 has been used, then 100° M leads to the companion buoy Bb3, after which the same applies. The channel is followed, red marks to port and greens to starboard when going east, to Bb11, the last of the buoys and the end of Bants Balje. Here there is a branch leading north and then east, which is a traditional and still much-used anchorage, the Slapersbucht. It is not buoyed, but easily found by sounding, and provides good holding in 2–3 m, with shelter from the surrounding shoals at all but high tide: a good place to waste two or three hours on the way west, so as to get a fair tide up to Delfzijl.

From Bb11 the channel becomes the Norddeicher Wattfahrwasser and is marked only by withies, though these are well laid and numerous. In 1978 I found 2.2 m depth at the watershed at a mean tide, which means 2.0 at HW neaps and 2.4 m at HW springs. I have used this channel for many years and never found less: I only mention this in so much detail because the German yachting pilot of the area, usually accurate, gives depths of 1.4 to 1.8 m which would be rather off-putting if they were not over-pessimistic. (Remember, however, the remarks above about the variations in tide levels caused by wind: with a strong easterly blowing those figures would be about right.)

Once over the watershed, the withies are followed northwards to B13/Bb14, from where the deep-water channel leads north to Norderney, or south to Norddeich.

An alternative route, most useful when travelling between Borkum and Norderney, lies some miles to the north. This is the Memmert Balje, beginning in the Osterems just south of the small island of Memmert (landing prohibited), and leading east (M buoys and then withies) to a point a mile SE of the east end of Juist, where it joins the Busetief, the main Norderney-Norddeich channel. It carries 1.7 to 2.0 m and in conjunction with the Borkum watt provides a good short passage between the two islands, though with the two watersheds 11 miles apart, the tides have to be judged exactly.

Juist

Least often used is the Juister Wattfahrwasser, running close along the south coast of Juist. This is mainly used for visiting that island and carries 1.6 to 1.9 m. There is no semblance of a yacht harbour on Juist; visitors anchor a cable south of the west part of the town, $\frac{1}{2}$ mile east of the massive steamer pier, but even at HW there is very little water. In suitable weather one can anchor in deep water at the

Juist, with *Kuri Moana* aground on the east end of the island, a perfect place for a picnic or a swim. Note the withy planted near the low water line. Beyond the off-lying shoal a ferry is making for Norddeich.

east end of the island, but this means 3 miles of rough walking to the small town.

Except for the specialist with unlimited time, I would consider Juist as one of the islands to be missed out of an itinerary, although the anchorage at the east end provides an ideal place for a picnic and a swim in good weather, perhaps as. a day excursion from Norderney, or on the way between there and Norddeich.

Norddeich

Famous as the home of the most important German coastal radio station, Norddeich is also useful as a place to stock up on German charts, as it has an excellent stockist in the shape of Fritz H. Venske, who are also first-class chandlers, overlooking the harbour. The approach between two breakwaters over a mile long presents no problems. At the end of the breakwaters the harbour divides, and yachts should proceed into the east harbour, on the port hand. Here there is a small yacht harbour, but they give the impression of not anticipating visitors, and in 1978 I found no vacant moorings there.

Norddeich. Yachts berth in the east harbour, on the left of the picture. The railway/ferry terminal is at right centre; diesel fuel in the west harbour, seen on the right.

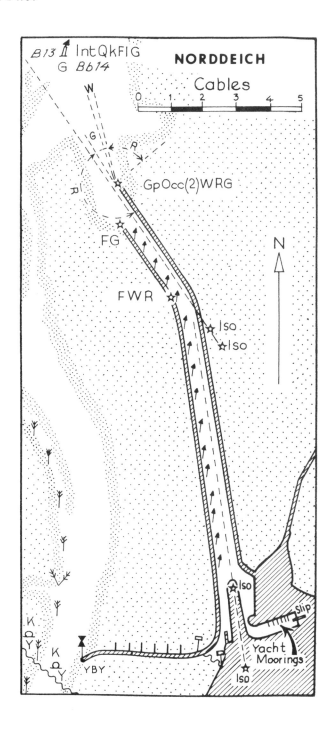

However, it is usually possible to find a fishing boat that is not going out the next day and lie alongside.

There is a yacht club, open lunchtimes and evenings, and a diesel bunker-station in the west harbour (dries at LW). There are restaurants near the harbour, and a railway station with trains to main German towns. Shops for basic supplies can be found about 200 m west of the west harbour along Hafenstrasse. Petrol only from garage, in cans. Venske, mentioned above (tel. (04931) 8001), also undertake hull and mechanical repairs. The town is really only the port of Norden, 2 miles to the SE, and Norddeich itself sprawls inconclusively without ever really coming to anything: it is useful mainly for its rail links and for charts, chandlery or repairs. A new yacht harbour with 4–500 berths is to be built west of the existing harbour and should be in operation in time for the 1980 season.

Norderney

This is one of the most important and highly developed of the German island harbours: it is now unrecognizable from the mid-1960s, when on my first visit a yacht had to tie up, usually alongside several others, and take the mud – a dangerous process as yachts that float level with each other often dry out to quite different heights.

From buoy B13/Bb14, the main route is down the Busetief to B1, across to the green Busetief buoy B11, and then ESE up the Riffgat. Near HW it is possible to cut across by a watt-channel called the Legde, sailing from B16 to L8 and following the L-series buoys to

Norderney: main lighthouse (and a typical withy).

Norderney entrance.

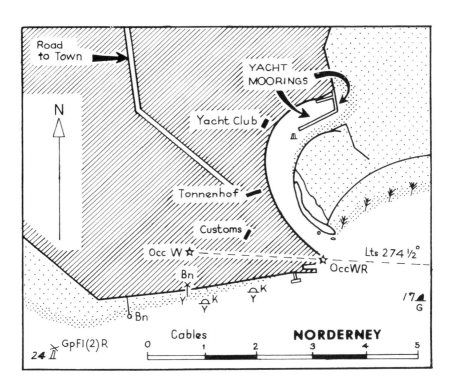

Norderney: approaching the yacht harbour. The low breakwater
at the right of the picture submerges at high water.

Legde 1, which lies in the Riffgat near the harbour entrance.
However, there is only 1.5 m depth at HW neaps (1.9 at HW
springs), and as the bottom is rocky it would be unwise to attempt
the passage in rough conditions, which means in fresh or strong
winds between W and N. In good weather the passage saves a couple
of miles, the last of which is often a slow plug into a strong ebb.

The harbour is invisible when approached from the west, but steer
to keep at least 100 m from the ferry pier, and keep on ENE until the
entrance suddenly opens up. Beware strong cross-tides in the entrance, and unexpected manoeuvres by large vessels leaving the
harbour, who often have to make sharp alterations of course to
prepare for the effects of the stream outside.

The yacht moorings are at the far end of the harbour, consisting
of a long L-shaped pontoon to which you moor bow-on with the
stern to posts. There are moorings outside as well as inside the
pontoon, and to the SW of the pontoon there are posts where one
can lie if there is no room, though a dinghy is then needed to go
ashore. Depth varies between 1.5 and 2 m at LW springs.

A small yacht club has toilets, bar and snacks. Very large or deep-
draft yachts lie to the quay nearby: make fast temporarily and
contact the harbourmaster. Water on the pontoons, diesel from
pump on the quay, petrol also available.

One of the features of this harbour is the Wasser- und Schif-
fahrtsamt in the Tonnenhof. This is one of the major buoyage and
lighthouse centres, and they are delighted to be visited and to supply

yachtsmen with the very latest information on buoyage, often long before it appears even in German *Notices to Mariners*.

The town is less than a mile from the harbour, and has good shops and excellent restaurants. It is a pleasant town: typically German seaside in style, and containing a very high proportion of German businessmen who haven't seen their knees for twenty years. I remember one whose remarkable tummy so overhung his very short shorts that, as he approached along the pavement, I thought he was stark naked apart from his inevitable yachting cap and plimsolls!

NORDERNEY TO LANGEOOG

Turning east once more from Norderney, there is only one main channel, and it is one of the deepest of all the watt-passages. East from the harbour, the Riffgat runs close along the island shore, and is well marked by buoys and withies. The watershed lies a mile east of the last buoy, no. 38, and carries about 1.9 m at HW neaps or 2.2 m at HW springs. From Norddeich there is a short-cut via the Wagengat, which comes out in the Riffgat between buoys 28 and 30, but this carries only 1.5 to 1.8 m. The Norderneyer Wattfahrwasser, as the watt part of the channel is called, leads into the Baltrum Seegat, which gives access to the harbours of Baltrum and Nessmersiel.

The Norderney Seegat
Though one of the best of the Seegats in the German islands, this is still no place to be in the wrong weather. The main channel, the Dove Tief, is approached from the buoy of that name, which lies about 2 miles offshore, roughly north of the eastern end of the town. The channel leads south for $1\frac{1}{2}$ miles, and then bears SW to clear the end of the island, after which it follows the shore. In normal conditions an eastbound yacht can safely bear away onto course after reaching buoy no. 4 on the way out. Depths change after every gale, but there is usually between $1\frac{1}{2}$ and 2 m at LW springs over the shallowest part of the channel, which lies between buoys nos. 5 and 3. I would avoid the channel in winds between NW and NE above force 5; and if over force 4 the passage should be made before HW, even if this means bucking the last of the flood by leaving Norderney an hour before HW.

A lesser channel, the Schluchter, leads out to the west, and is useful because of that. It is much more exposed, however, and must be avoided in fresh or strong winds *or swell* from between W and N.

Baltrum. In a strong southwesterly like this the harbour is no
place for a visiting yacht.

The least depth is usually a metre or less at LW springs, and I
remember a period when it almost disappeared. However, in 1978 it
was well buoyed and a very handy fine-weather channel.

Baltrum
Very much the smallest of the German islands (apart from the
virtually uninhabited Memmert), Baltrum is a pretty island with an
attractive small town of about 600 inhabitants.

The entrance to the harbour is straightforward enough, but
coming from the west it is important to go north to the red buoy
north of the Baltrumer Balje 1 buoy, before turning SE and steering
to leave to port the beacon with a red can topmark which marks the
end of the mole. Once this is rounded, steer to leave the withies
about 10 m to port, and enter the small harbour. The yacht
moorings are on the SE side of the harbour, which dries to hard sand
at LW so keel yachts must take appropriate precautions. There is a
little over 2 m at mean HW on the moorings.

The yacht club has a building overlooking the harbour, with
showers and toilets; water can be had there or from the steamer pier
on the NW side of the harbour. Simple stores from the small town $\frac{1}{4}$
mile NNE of the harbour. This is a pleasant place and well worth a
visit, but the harbour is badly exposed to winds from between S and

SW, and if they are strong it can become positively dangerous during the hours around HW, so avoid the harbour if there is any prospect of such conditions arising.

Nessmersiel

In contrast to Baltrum, this harbour offers good shelter in all weathers, although it is not convenient for stores. From Baltrumer Balje 1, the approach is down the Nessmersieler Balje. Steer to leave Nessmersiel 1 close to starboard, after which the channel is marked by starboard buoys (N3, etc) and beacons, leading to the end of the Leitdamm, the protective submersible breakwater typical of all these ports. This is marked by a light beacon (Occ W), and the lie of the wall is marked by beacons. Keep over towards the withies which

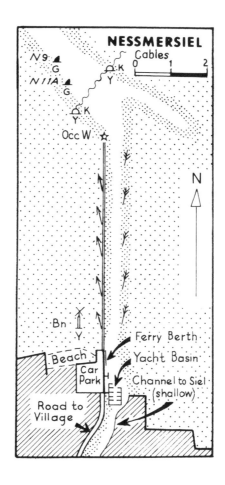

Nessmersiel: leaving the harbour.

mark the E side of the channel, as the best water lies some way E of the dam.

Entering the harbour, a steamer pier and a pontoon for small commercial vessels lie on the solid west side of the harbour, while the east side is salt-marsh. A little further south lie the pontoons of the Nordsee Yachtclub Nessmersiel (NYCN), where visitors moor as space allows. There is about $\frac{1}{2}$ m of water in the entrance channel at mean LW, and around $1\frac{1}{2}$ m in the yacht basin, according to how recently it was last dredged. The small town and the siel (sluice) itself lies about $1\frac{1}{2}$ miles to the south: vessels drawing less than 1 m can sail up a narrow channel and take the mud just north of the siel, and close to the village.

Baltrum's Seegat – the Wichter Ee
This is one of the shallowest and most dangerous of all the Seegats between the German islands. Even in the narrow channel there is less than 1 m of water at LW, and there are wrecks and other obstructions in the area. The passage should not be attempted.

The passage east from Baltrum is one of the shallower watt-passages, probably because of the relatively small size of its protective island. In 1978 I found only 1.6 m at HW neaps, which would indicate 1.9 at HW springs. On the other hand it is a short and straightforward passage, so there is little problem in timing the tide accurately. The channel is entered by steering from Baltrum Balje 1 direct for B2, the red pillar buoy that lies 2 cables to the SSE, after which first the remaining red B-series buoys, and then withies, are left to port. After the watershed the same red buoy series begins again with B18, and more buoys and withies lead to A13/B24, the junction with the Accumer Ee, the main deep-water channel west of Langeoog. This system offers the luxury of three ports instead of the usual two: the island harbour of Langeoog, and Dornumersiel and Bensersiel on the mainland.

Langeoog

This has always been one of my favourite stopping-places, and I was delighted to see in 1978 that the members of the yacht club were constructing a large network of brand-new yacht pontoons, entirely by voluntary effort. I was assured that these would be ready for the 1979 season, and accommodate 200 yachts. They also said that there would be 1.2 to 1.5 m at LW, but this depends on dredging, as the

Langeoog. *Kuri Moana* is lying bows-on to the wooden jetty, with stern lines to posts. The first of the new pontoons can just be seen to the left of picture.

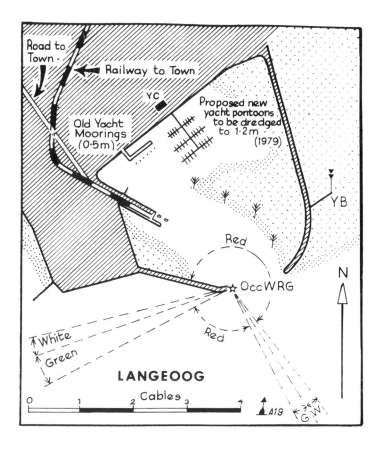

area where the pontoons are to be laid has always dried, so perhaps it would be rash to rely on that quite so soon.

A straight course can be steered from A13/B24 to the harbour entrance, leaving further green A buoys to starboard. The entrance is without hazards, but once inside the harbour pay close attention to the line of withies on the starboard hand. They mark the edge of a very steep-to bank, with less than a metre of water on it at HW springs. Steer to leave the ferry pier which projects from the west side of the harbour fairly close to port, and then turn N and moor to the wooden jetty (these moorings dried in 1978, although the chart shows water), or turn NE into the new pontoon area, depth as yet unknown.

There is a small club-restaurant just north of the old yacht moorings, which will fill water cans. Stores only from the town. This is a 1½ mile hike along a very sandy road; no motor vehicles are

The Westturm on Wangerooge.

allowed on the island, but a pleasant if rather expensive way to bring home the bacon is to hire a pony trap for the return journey. There are also trains between the harbour and the town when the steamers are in: the schedule varies with tide, but it is often possible to travel to town and back by train. Enquire at the harbour office at the west corner of the harbour.

The town is pretty and has good shops and restaurants: as with all the islands these are far more than the population of 2000 would justify, as in summer there are four or five visitors for every native. Do not miss the view from the dunes by the water tower to the NW of the town: if it is blowing a stiff nor'wester, the surf on the shoals in the Seegat is an impressive sight, and one can also get a good view of the watts, and at low water see the lie of the channels.

It was here that my friends Ralf Heyen and Arne Gebhardt, both twelve in 1978 and island born, taught me this old Ostfriesische poem, designed as a mnemonic for the names and sequence of the islands:

Wangeroog het ein hohen Torn
Spiekeroog het sein Nom verlorn
Langeoog dat is noch wat
Baltrum is ein Sandfat.
Up Norderney, dor givt ein Schleft full Brei
Up Juist sind all Kojen güst
Und kom we den no Börken
Da steckens uns mit Förken!

A free translation might go:

Wangerooge has a tower of fame
Spiekeroog has lost its name
Langeoog is a worthy land
Baltrum's just a cask of sand.
They feed you gruel on Norderney
On Juist, the farmers' cows are dry,
But the friendly men of the Isle of Borkum
Set upon strangers and pitchfork 'em!

My apologies to the slandered men of Borkum, but it is interesting to note that the beautiful old tower which begins the poem still stands proudly on Wangerooge.

Dornumersiel
The more westerly of the two mainland harbours south of Langeoog, this is one of the most important of all the 'siels', as it has a full-scale yacht harbour providing absolute shelter and almost

Dornumersiel: entrance at high water.

Dornumersiel: entrance to the yacht harbour. The main channel comes in from left of picture: below half-tide the turn can be tricky, as there is not a lot of room.

always a comfortable berth alongside. From A13/B24, steer E for $\frac{1}{2}$ mile to buoy A15 (green with north cone topmark). This is also numbered Accumersiel Balje 2, and from here the channel is marked by AB buoys and withies (leave to port). At green AB3 (Int Qk Fl Green), turn slightly S for the first of the besoms marking the W side

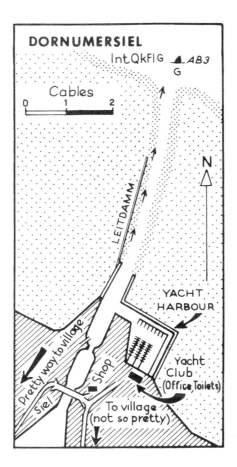

of the final approach channel. There is the usual Leitdamm, but the channel lies well away from it and the beacons are laid in the sand rather than indicating the run of the barrier itself.

Entering between the main pierheads, the yacht harbour lies about 100 m inside, on the port (east) side. The entrance is narrow, and one should keep well to the west side of the main channel to get maximum room for lining up. There is a decimetre or two of water in the entrance channel even at LW springs, so the average yacht can get in and out 2 hours before or after LW, when there would be a minimum of 1.3 m, and usually more.

Once through the narrow entrance, the yacht harbour opens up into a considerable basin some 200 m wide and with numerous pontoons. Visitors should secure on the port side along the NE pontoon, and confirm at the harbour office. At the same time borrow a key to the harbour, as it is efficiently fenced in and normally locked, but one can wander out while the gate is open to let a car through, and find oneself locked out on returning. I did!

Toilets at the harbourmaster's hut near the gate; water on all the south pontoons. Diesel is available, but only with a tax-free permit, available at larger ports such as Norderney. There are restaurants nearby, and a small but good self-service shop which opens Sundays. Otherwise the immediate area is bleak, with a huge camping area but no houses. However, a nice rose-bowered ¾ mile walk along the west side of the canal leads to the village of Westeraccumersiel, where the Nordsee Hotel (tel (04933) 405) is a good bet: good Italian cooking by the owner, Signor Di Scala, and reasonable prices.

Bensersiel

This harbour lies SE of Langeoog harbour, but still within the same deep-water system. Cut straight from A19, outside Langeoog, to A21 (green conical buoy) and thence to A23. From here besoms and beacons to starboard and withies to port lead up the long channel between two Leitdamms: note particularly that the light beacon is on the *east* dam, which is submerged well before HW.

After a good mile of entrance channel, a solid pier will be seen on the starboard hand, and another 250 m brings the visitor to the entrance of the main yacht harbour. This lies on the starboard (west)

Bensersiel entrance.

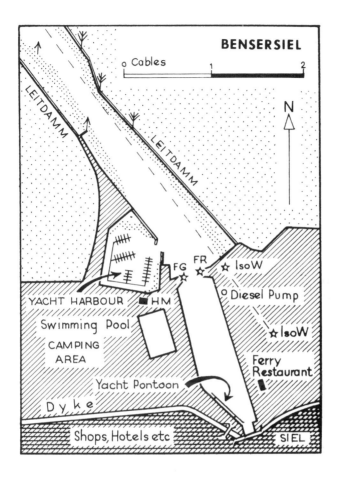

side, just before the narrow entrance to the main inner harbour. There is 1–1½ m of water at LW in the yacht harbour, according to the time since it was last dredged. It is also possible to lie alongside at the SW end of the inner harbour, also 1–2 m deep at LW. Diesel on the east pier, petrol from garage. This is a siel with a proper village, and there are good shops, hotels and restaurants close to the harbour; there is also a considerable boatbuilder, Harle-Yachtbau, a couple of miles away at Esens, which can organize repairs (tel (04971) 1760 or 2136).

Langeoog's Seegat – the Accumer Ee
This is one of the better Seegats, with a least depth of about 2½ m at LW springs, and without involving a long diversion to east or west before clearing the shoals. This makes Langeoog a good starting

Bensersiel: the inner yacht moorings.

point for, or landfall from, Helgoland. From the red and white Accumer Ee offing buoy (Iso 8 sec) a course of 125° M leads into the channel. However, if buoys A1 and A2 are identified positively it is safe to steer straight for them, as they lie well outside the shoal area. The channel is closely buoyed and only presents problems in wind-against-tide conditions, but in this case the sands lie in such a way that a strong S to SE wind against the flood can be almost as nasty as the onshore wind over the ebb for which all these entrances are famous. In such conditions the Westerbalje at the east end of Langeoog (see Otzumer Balje, pages 89–90) is a very much safer and pleasanter way in. On the other hand, in 1972 I was caught in a SW gale off this coast after a long and exhausting passage out of the Elbe with youngish children aboard, and although the seas looked very dramatic, they smoothed out as I approached the inner part of the channel just before the water got dangerously shallow, as the Westerriff began to provide a breakwater. But entering in such conditions should *only* ever be attempted under reliable power, while depth sounding continuously. Even then the skipper must remember that turning back can be the most dangerous manoeuvre in shoaling water, so one must be prepared to abort the attempt when there is still plenty of water under the keel: I would suggest at the very least 2 m at the bottom of the troughs. But with these precautions, many of these harbours can safely be entered in heavy weather, as long as the wind is even slightly offshore.

LANGEOOG TO THE JADE

There are two main channels leading east from Langeoog. The northern Langeooger Wattfahrwasser has about 2.2 to 2.5 m depth at HW. From the harbour entrance steer ENE for LW2 (a red pillar buoy) and follow the red LW buoys and then withies to the watershed, about a mile west of the eastern end of the island. Once in the deep Hullbalje turn N for LW3/St8 (green conical buoy with north cone) and so to LW8 (red) and 9/LW10 (green), before turning SE into the Schillbalje, the main sea channel between Langeoog and Spiekeroog. The area around 9/LW10 is exposed to winds from W to N, and this passage should be avoided in heavy weather from that quarter.

The alternative is the Neuharlingersieler Wattfahrwasser, which is about 1.8–2.1 m deep at HW. A series of buoys are followed past the entrance of Bensersiel to A24/Stüverslegde 2, from where it is possible to branch north into the Hullbalje over a 1.5–1.8 m watt. The more southerly line of withies is the main one, however, and this leads up to the watershed, where the channel is known as the Backlegde, and so into deep water near the northern end of the Neuharlingersiel Leitdamm. Bound for Wangerooge in one hop, it is wiser to take the southern route, as the distance between the first and last watersheds is less. Either way, though, with a draft of 5 ft (1.5 m) or less, this is one of the easier two-island hops.

Spiekeroog
Reputedly one of the prettiest of the German islands, Spiekeroog unfortunately offers only a small ferry harbour which dries out, and where the heavy swell in winds from S to SW makes it a risky place to visit unless the weather is set fair. The approach and entry are straightforward, although it can be rough off the SW side of the island in strong NW winds, especially in the first 2 hours after HW. No facilities in the harbour; the town is reached by rail, or by a half-hour walk along the railway track.

In a bilge-keel or flat-bottomed boat a more practical way to visit the island, except in winds from E to SW through S, is to proceed at HW into the bay immediately south of the town. At an average HW there is 1.5 m of water well in towards the shore, and a yacht can lie to its anchor and dry out in perfect shelter from W or N winds; indeed, with draft of 1.2 m or less it is often possible to nose into one of the creeks and get ashore via a boarding plank only half a mile from the town. But do not, of course, risk being neaped, which will happen if you have cut it fine, and the wind then turns easterly and lowers the mean tide level.

Neuharlingersiel

Along most of this coast the dykes have been moved to seaward to reclaim more land, and so most of the siel villages are modern, often with more attractive old ones a mile inland. Neuharlingersiel, however, is an example of an original siel harbour, and it is one of the most charming places to be found on the Frisian mainland.

The approach is easy from the Baklegde, whose marked channel leads straight past the light beacon (Occ) on the north end of the Leitdamm. From Spiekeroog, the Schillbalje leads by way of buoys no. 11 (Gp Occ (2) Green) and no. 14 (red) to 13/A25 (Int Qk Fl Green) from where a course may be steered for the light beacon. The

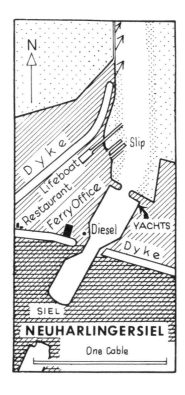

Neuharlingersiel: not the best equipped, but certainly the most
picturesque of the siel harbours.

entrance channel lies close east of the Leitdamm, which is marked by
posts with north cones. Yachts may lie on the east side of the harbour immediately inside the entrance, alongside the quay: if there is
no room then it is a case of finding a fishing boat which is not going
out. There is about $\frac{3}{4}$ m of water in the entrance channel at mean
LW, and a little less in the harbour, so it is available at most states of
the tide, and the mud is soft enough for keels to sink in. Good shops
and restaurants in the village. There is a diesel pump on the west
quay, but only for those with duty-free Customs permits. This is
another of the locations where *The Riddle of the Sands* was filmed,
as the inner harbour looks just as it did when Erskine Childers was
cruising there at the turn of the century, so try not to miss seeing this
unique survival if you are in the area.

Spiekeroog's Seegat – the Otzumer Balje
This Seegat is little used, not so much because there is anything
difficult about it as that the deep-water system to which it gives
access has no important harbour. Like so many, the channel has a
western branch, here called the Westerbalje, with W-series buoys.
The bar (1.3 m at LW springs) of this channel is further inshore than

usual and is protected from the NW, so in NW winds it is the more comfortable of the two. The approach to the bar is buoyed at intervals of about $\frac{1}{2}$ mile from the red and white unlit Westerbalje buoy.

The main channel, the Otzumer Balje, carries just over 2 m at LW springs at its shallowest part, which is about a mile south of the red and white Otzumer Balje buoy (Fl 4 sec). Here the shoals to the sides have a metre of water at LW, but further south between the islands the channel is narrow and exceptionally deep, running between high drying banks. The tide can run at up to 4 knots in this stretch, so it is wise to have the engine going if entering with a light following wind; the apparent wind can drop to nothing in these conditions, and I have seen a yacht with a collapsed spinnaker miss one of the channel buoys only by inches and pure luck.

Spiekeroog to Wangerooge

There are two watt-passages between Spiekeroog and Wangerooge, and if that is where you are going there is nothing to choose between them either in depth or length. In either case proceed up the Schillbalje past buoy 13/A25, and leave the subsequent red buoys and withies on the north side as far as no. 26, which has a cylindrical topmark. This buoy marks the division of the two watt-passages, and is also named Spiekerooger Watt 2.

The more northerly passage is the Spiekerooger Wattfahrwasser, and it winds over a long course, with a depth over the watershed of 2.0 to 2.3 m, until buoy SW4 is reached $\frac{1}{2}$ mile SE of the eastern point of Spiekeroog. From here steer carefully to SW6: the mouth of the Wattfahrwasser here tends to vary in depth and layout, and it is worth keeping the echo sounder going. Once past this bar, a course to H5/SW8 leads into the Dove Harle, the main deep of Wangerooge.

The more southerly passage from Spiekerooger Watt 2 buoy is the Harlesieler Wattfahrwasser, and is the channel to use if going to Harlesiel. It also has 2.0 to 2.3 m at HW on its watershed. Watch out for small uncharted green conical buoys, which in 1978 were inserted among withies along the east part of the channel. These should be left on the north side as they are marking the channel from the sea up to Harlesiel, and are not marks for the watt-passage, where they would be south side markers. It will be seen that the new system has still not removed all confusions! Proceeding NE past H13/H Watt 1, take care to go all the way to H9. This must be passed on its east side, and the channel is narrow there, so any attempt to cut the corner to H16 may leave you aground.

Wangerooge

This harbour is uncomfortable and often dangerous in heavy weather from any quarter except the north, and if the forecast is bad take my advice and stick to the dull but safe alternative of Harlesiel. In good weather, however, it is a most useful harbour, well-placed for making an accurately timed departure for the Jade, the Elbe or Helgoland, so it is much to be hoped that the plans for a new yacht harbour, long on the file, will one day be brought to fruition.

If coming from the southern route or Harlesiel, proceed N along the Harle to H5/SW8. From here it is safe to make good a straight track to D3/T2, but if the tide is making, back-bearings must be used to ensure that you are not set SE onto the NW tip of the Hoher Rücken shoal. Once at D3/T2, a straight course for D4 and D6 leads to the harbour entrance, marked by withies on its west side. Inside, yachts are forbidden to lie at the railway quay on the west side, but must use the rough wooden pier on the east side, north of the elbow, with approx. 1.5 m at LW springs. This pier has unexpected projections and indentations, and the inside boat of each trot (there is room for three) must keep watch as the tide falls, particularly in westerly winds. There is severe swell in southerly winds, and in

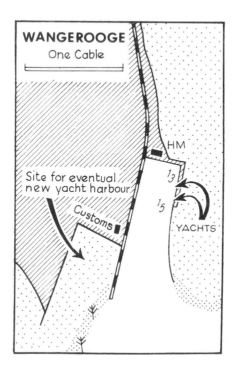

WANGEROOGE
One Cable
Site for eventual new yacht harbour
Customs
HM
YACHTS

Wangerooge: entrance. Beware strong cross-tides until inside the pierheads.

Wangerooge at high water after a rough night. The train is picking up passengers from the first ferry, while the yachtsmen examine their scrapes and scratches.

easterly gales waves break clear over the east pier near HW. There are no facilities at the harbour; the harbourmaster collects dues, but takes no other notice of yachts unless they break regulations. The town, with shops and restaurants, is reached by rail only, and the walk along the track is at least an hour. Closer by, the old tower offers a picturesque place for a picnic. Shallow-draft vessels can dry out at anchor in the bay NNE of the harbour where at HW there is 1.2–1.6 m of water close to the shore according to tide. A few besoms mark the best route. The planned new yacht harbour would be to the west of the western pier, and would offer better shelter and numerous berths. Considering the strategic importance of the position of Wangerooge, a day sail from so many different important ports, let us hope that the fairly modest works that would be involved are not delayed too much longer.

Harlesiel
The harbour lies 4 miles SSW of Wangerooge, and is reached via the Carolinensieler Balje. From H13/Harlesiel Watt 1 buoy the channel is closely buoyed as far as the light beacon (Fl 6 sec) at the end of the Leitdamm. Note, however, that there are besoms and north cone beacons marking the west side of the channel before this is reached. After the light beacon, keep fairly close down the dam, marked by posts, and enter the outer harbour. There is 0.4 m at LW springs in the entrance channel.

When the water level is below half tide (and with an easterly wind this can mean all but 2 hours either side of HW), if the large ferry leaves the harbour it has to keep to the centre of the channel, and its wash can throw an approaching yacht onto the breakwater. If the ferry is seen coming out at such a tide, therefore, a yacht should retreat if necessary and wait north of the light beacon until the ferry, which carries a black cylinder to show its right of way, is clear. Near HW, on the other hand, when the Leitdamm is submerged, beware of being set onto it, as the stream then ceases to run up and down the channel, and cross-currents develop.

Yachts are allowed to moor for the night on the inner part of the west quay, but this is a restless berth, and it seems better, unless arriving very late, to lock into the canal which leads south to the old sluice at Carolinensiel. Here yachts can moor alongside either side for 300 m, which allows plenty of room. Diesel (with duty-free permit) and water on the west quay. Two hotels on the west side of the inner harbour, and modern (but in 1978 filthy) toilets between. Modest shops. I have eaten particularly well and reasonably at Up'n Diek (Up on the Dyke), a restaurant on the dyke just east of the

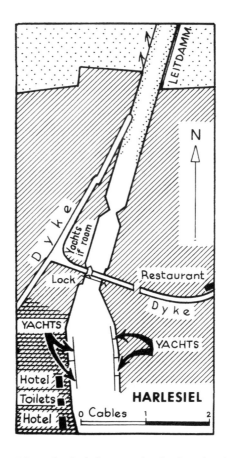

Harlesiel entrance. Note the Leitdamms, both already almost awash.

Harlesiel: the moorings inside the lock. The lifting bridge can be seen just to the left of the harbour control building, also recognisable in the previous picture.

bridge over the lock.

There is 2 m of water alongside in the inner harbour, but there may be less in the lock, and if arriving near LW it is worth enquiring what the depth is over the sill. Remember that the water level falls in the lock when locking in: the fall can be nearly 2 m and quite rapid, so keep the lines ready to pay out!

Wangerooge's Seegat – the Dove Harle

The most important hazard of this Seegat is the mile-long break-water that projects WSW from the western tip of the island of Wangerooge and is clearly but not very conspicuously marked on the chart. Yachts beating in against a light wind with a fair tide have often come to grief on this, as the depthsounder gives no warning.

However, as long as the buoyed channel is kept to, there are no problems, although the very fast stream can make navigation a rather more hurried affair than some skippers are used to. The channel is a straightforward north-south one, with a 2 m bar near its north end, and closely buoyed from the red and white Harle (Fl 8 sec) offing buoy. I would avoid entering in onshore winds over force 6 (and in force 5 or 6 only enter in the 2 hours before HW), or

95

leaving in onshore winds above low force 5, but it is one of the most reliable of the second-rank Seegats.

Wangerooge to the mouth of the Jade

The main channel east from Wangerooge harbour involves going west against the stream as far as D3/T2, before making south for T1 and T3 into the Telegraphenbalje. At over half tide, however, it is safe to cut across halfway between T1 and T3, as long as enough power is available to get up-tide if the soundings shoal too far. Alternatively, there is a withied short-cut that starts off east from the harbour, and then bends south to join the Telegraphenbalje, but this had silted up in 1978 and local opinion was that there was no more than 1.6 to 1.9 m depth at HW.

The main watershed lies 2–3 miles east of the harbour, and has 2.1 to 2.4 m at HW. Withies mark the north of the channel east of buoy T3, and these lead all the way to the eastern tip of Wangerooge. From here the buoyed Blaue Balje leads out to sea, but this is a route that few yachts would ever take. Cross to red buoy B8, leaving a yellow and red tower (uncharted in 1978) close to starboard on the

Oldoog lighthouse.

way, and from there follow successively red buoys, green buoys and withies down the Minsener Balje and across the Minseneroog Watt to B20, which lies in the open Jade. This last watershed has 2.0–2.3 m at HW. On the passage, red buoys and withies mark the NE side of the channel, and green buoys the west: all should be approached closely, as the channel is less than 100 m wide in places. There is another channel keeping close to the south of Oldoog, whose lighthouse (photo) is a useful landmark in the area, but this is unmarked and has only 1.5–1.8 m at HW, so there is little incentive to use it, as it saves only $\frac{1}{2}$ mile at the most. From B20 one may turn south into the Jade, or a course 6 miles NE past the Mellumplate light and Mellum 4 buoy leads into the outer Weser (unfortunately with the very strong ebb well established by then). These rivers are dealt with in a later chapter.

IV · Helgoland

Chart: German 49 (88 is not necessary: see plan below)

As Helgoland is the smallest of the inhabited German islands covered by this book, it seems curious that it should have a section all to itself, but its separateness, and its importance to the cruising man, seem to justify this.

The island was a British possession from 1807 to 1890, and as late as 1978 there were still one or two surviving natives who were born British citizens. The RAF virtually obliterated the old town on the Oberland, and so all the buildings on the island are now post-war. The spoken dialect is a version of Fries, and a sailor from here can understand one from Harlingen if they both speak their local dialects, although the Dutchman may understand no German, and the German no Dutch.

Helgoland lies 23 miles north of Wangerooge, 20 miles NNW of the Alte Weser light tower which marks the mouths of the Jade and Weser rivers, and 13 miles NW of Elbe 1 lightvessel, which does the same for the Elbe.

Approaching from the south, the island appears cigar-shaped and can be seen for a great distance in good visibility, as the Oberland, the plateau which makes up the west of the island, is over 50 m high. Düne, on the other hand, the companion island $\frac{1}{2}$ mile to the east, is so low that it can only be seen for a mile or two. The only hazard that is likely to trouble a yacht is the 1 m wreck on the end of the Hogstean shoal, 4 cables south of the light on the end of the Süd-mole which forms the southern wall of the main harbour. The channel is well buoyed from the Helgoland buoy a mile to the south, and at night there are leading lights on Düne which lead safely up the channel to Hogstean-3 buoy (Fl G 4 sec), from where it is safe to steer straight for the entrance (Gp Occ (2) Red and Occ Green).

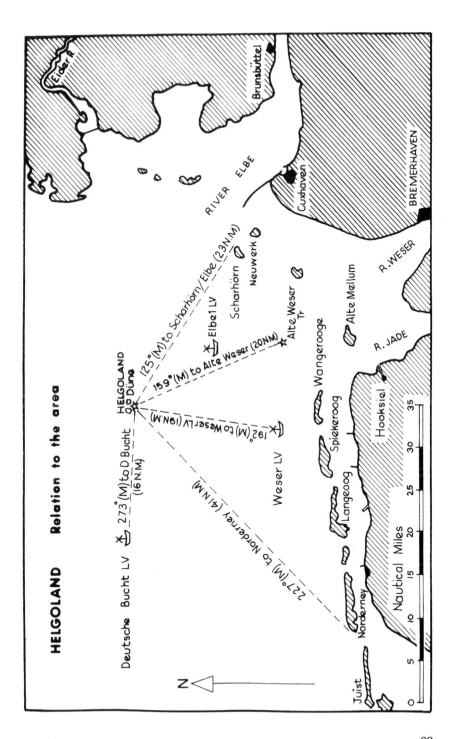

HELGOLAND   Relation to the area

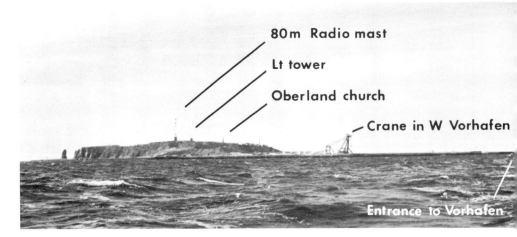

Helgoland from the SE. Düne is out of the picture to the right.

The northern Oberland on Helgoland.

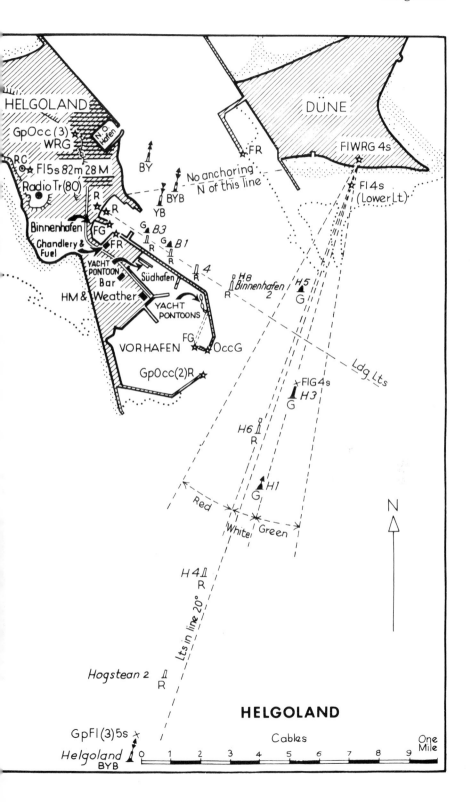

HELGOLAND

DÜNE

GpOcc(3)
WRG

O.Hafen

RC
Fl5s 82m 28M

Radio Tr(80)

FR

FlWRG 4s

BY

No anchoring
N of this line

Fl 4s
(Lower Lt)

BYB

R
R

YB

Binnenhafen

FG

G B3

Chandlery &
Fuel

FR

G B1

R

YACHT
PONTOON

Bar

R 4

Südhafen

HM & Weather

H8
Binnenhafen
2

H5
G

YACHT
PONTOONS

VORHAFEN

FG

OccG

GpOcc(2)R

Ldg Lts

FlG 4s
H3
G

H6
R

H1
G

Red

White

Green

H4
R

Lts in line 20°

Hogstean 2
R

HELGOLAND

GpFl(3)5s

Cables

One
Mile

Helgoland
BYB

0   1   2   3   4   5   6   7   8   9

N

The approach from the north is more difficult, but is only likely to be used if a poor landfall has been made after a long passage from the west, or if coming south from Denmark or Norway. Here either the black and yellow Nathurn (V Qk Fl) or yellow-black-yellow Sellebrun (V Qk Fl (9) 10 sec) buoys must be identified, after which the Nordreede channel (N-series buoys) can be followed. The Nathurn buoy lies almost exactly on a bearing of 315° M from Helgoland light, so if the island is sighted to the southward proceed E or W until the light bears SE (135° M) and then approach on that bearing, when the Nathurn will be on the track. This assumes good visibility, as the buoy lies 3 miles from the light, and the dangerous shoals which project NW from Düne extend nearly as far. In bad visibility, if needing to approach from the north, get the radiobeacon bearing 155° M and approach on that line, temporarily turning east whenever within the 5 m line if nothing has been sighted. I have used this technique to bring me right into the main anchorage east of the

Südhafen, Helgoland. The main yacht moorings are in the Vorhafen, just to the left of the Südhafen entrance in the distance, where a couple of Bermudan sails can be seen. The extra walking distance is clear from this angle.

town in visibility of 100 m. In normal conditions, after approaching from the north, proceed SSE midway between the islands (beware heavy launch traffic between anchored steamers and shore: they are not inclined to give way!) to Hogstean 5 buoy (green conical) $\frac{1}{2}$ mile south of Düne, after which a straight course may be steered for the harbour entrance.

Once in the Vorhafen, the main yacht moorings will be seen in the NE part of the harbour. Yachts moor with bows to a barge, used as a pontoon, and stern to a buoy, and a good long stern warp is needed. Alternatively (and in my experience, preferably) one may continue through the small entrance in the north corner of the Vorhafen into the Südhafen. Here there is a pontoon attached to a high catwalk, where yachts may moor two or three abreast. There are berths for 80 yachts in the Vorhafen, and about 25 in the Südhafen. The same rather high dues apply in both harbours (DM8 for 8–16 m LOA in 1978). The advantage of the Südhafen is greater shelter (in strong east to southeast winds both harbours are most uncomfortable, but the outer one can be positively hellish: I have had to take my crew ashore because they were seasick on the moorings!) and a much shorter walk into town. But the ladders to the catwalk are very high at LW, and can be a problem for some people. Visitors should report to the harbour office on arrival: it is at the SW corner of the Südhafen. Diesel, petrol and water can be had from Hans Rickmers, who have a bunker-station in the Binnenhafen, approached along a buoyed channel which runs just north of the Ostmole. They are Cruising Association Boatmen, and are most helpful to all visitors, with exceptional stocks in the way of chandlery and a capacity to carry out repairs.

There are toilets and washbasins, but not showers, on the pontoon barges in the Vorhafen. The lack of showers is a disappointment, but I was assured in 1978 that a free toilet and shower block was to be built by the west corner of the Südhafen in time for the 1979 season. All other facilities are available: a most helpful weather station above the harbour office welcomes personal visits, and will give up-to-the-minute predictions, which I have found unusually accurate. Good shops in the main town, and drink and tobacco are sold at very low rates of duty, which makes them the cheapest in North Europe, even though the prices have risen sharply in the last few years. Good restaurants too, but in my opinion the best is on the Oberland. This is a fish restaurant called Lührs, 20 m up the hill from the top of the lift, whose upper station is easy to see even if you prefer to stroll up by the steps on a fine evening.

Helgoland is a pleasant and friendly place, though crowded

during the day. It is geared to visiting yachts, and offers almost everything which they might want. It is strategically placed for many routes, and I am always amazed how seldom it seems to be visited by British yachts.

I should perhaps end by mentioning that Düne harbour is banned to yachts, and that it is forbidden to land on that island from a private boat. It may only be visited by a regular ferry from Helgoland (Binnenhafen) or in the course of flying to or from the island, as the small airstrip is on Düne. But as it appears to be little more than an overgrown sand-dune (as its name implies), I doubt whether a visit would be very rewarding. I must confess that I have never bothered.

V · The Rivers Jade and Weser

Charts: German 2, 7, 4

These rivers are dealt with together, as they share a common mouth, at least as far as shoal-draft navigation is concerned, and in any case I would not expect many foreign visitors to make a great deal of use of the Weser, which has not much to recommend it as a cruising ground.

Coming from the west, the Weser lightvessel lies at the point where the decision between the two rivers is made. A course of 100° M leads into the Neue Weser marked by the Roter Sand light, while 130° M leads down to the Mellumerplate light and the Jade. From the north, for example from Helgoland or the Elbe, the best landmark is the magnificent Alte Weser light tower, which can often be seen from Elbe 1 lightvessel. From here the Weser entrance is open: for the Jade it is necessary to cross west to buoy A11, then north of the Roter Sand light to Mittelrinne 2, and thence south through the Mittelrinne into the Jade proper.

While not quite as dangerous as the Elbe, it must be remembered that the outer parts of both these estuaries are very rough in wind-over-tide conditions, and in particular they are dangerous in strong NW winds over the ebb tide. It can therefore be difficult to get out if the wind sets in hard from that quarter. It is always possible to get over the watt to Harlesiel, however, and make for the west in relative shelter until the weather improves.

THE JADE

Traditionally the Jade has been regarded as a river to be used by yachtsmen only as a refuge. Caught in a NW gale when coming

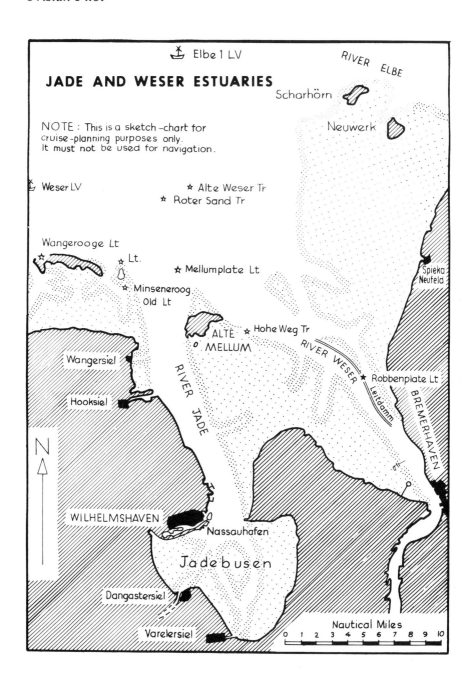

⚓ Elbe 1 LV

RIVER ELBE

JADE AND WESER ESTUARIES

Scharhörn

NOTE : This is a sketch-chart for
cruise-planning purposes only.
It must not be used for navigation.

Neuwerk

⚓ Weser LV

★ Alte Weser Tr
★ Roter Sand Tr

Wangerooge Lt

★ Lt.

Spieka
Neufeld

★ Mellumplate Lt

★ Minseneroog
Old Lt

ALTE
MELLUM

★ Hohe Weg Tr

RIVER WESER

RIVER JADE

Wangersiel

★ Robbenplate Lt

Leitdamm

BREMERHAVEN

Hooksiel

N
↑

WILHELMSHAVEN

Nassauhafen

Jadebusen

Dangastersiel

Nautical Miles

Varelersiel

0 1 2 3 4 5 6 7 8 9 10

The Alte Weser light tower, the most important seaward mark
in the Jade and Weser estuary.

south from Helgoland, or having failed to reach the Elbe, one might
run for shelter at Wilhelmshaven. The river still offers valuable
safety, although it must be remembered that in such conditions one
must on no account attempt to enter against the ebb. The seas under
such conditions are so high and steep that even a large yacht will
almost certainly get out of control. If caught in this unhappy
situation, stand off until low water (which at the mouth is about 1
hour before Wilhelmshaven), and only then approach nearer than
Jade buoys nos. 6 and 9, which lie about 2 miles north of
Wangerooge town.

Recent developments, however, make this river worth a visit in its
own right, and happily it is no longer necessary to go all the way to

the doubtful delights of Wilhelmshaven in order to find a berth. A mile south of the Schillighörn, Wangersiel now offers the possibility of a comfortable berth, and 3 miles further on Hooksiel provides the certainty of one.

Wangersiel (Horumersiel)
This pleasant small harbour was once called Horumersiel, and still shown as such on the chart. It is approached from buoy W3 (green conical) a rather small buoy 1 mile ESE of the Schillighörn light. From here besoms mark the north side of the channel, whose shallowest part is a hard sand bar close to the deep water of the river. Once over this there will be plenty of water to reach the harbour, but the deepest channel will often be found 10–20 m from the besoms. There is about 0.4 m in the shallowest part of the channel at LW springs.

Wangersiel. The best chance of a berth is on the starboard hand.
The sphere on the beach makes a good landmark.

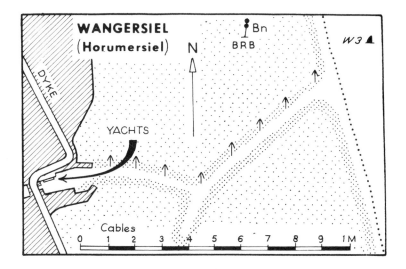

The moorings lie along the northern quay, with a pontoon at the west end, and the harbour is often very crowded. Visitors tend to cause some surprise, but everyone is friendly and room will be made if possible. Water on the yacht club pontoon, but no fuel. There is 1 to 1½ m in the harbour at LW: keelboats should not count on sinking into the bottom, but take appropriate precautions. Shops and restaurants in the town (Horumersiel) five minutes' walk away. There is some swell near HW in strong E winds.

Hooksiel
Three miles SSE of Wangersiel lies the outer harbour of Hooksiel. It is approached from Hooksiel 1 (Qk Fl Green), from where a course must be steered for the small H3 buoy outside the entrance. The water here can be shallow and the banks shift, so it is wise to proceed cautiously and sound. The outer harbour has about 1 m at LW springs, and so is available to most yachts at almost all times; the best water lies along the N quay except near the lock, where it is opposite the gates.

Yachts may lie in the outer harbour, but this is a busy and restless place. Most lock in: the lock opens at 0900, 1000, 1500, 1600 every day, with extra openings at 1700 on Fridays, and at 1700, 1800 and 1900 on Saturdays and Sundays (May–Sept). In 1978 charges were DM6 per locking for yachts of 8–12 m, so it comes a little expensive for one night.

Once through what must be one of the best locks for yachts in Europe, you find yourself in a lake nearly 2 miles long, with a

Hooksiel entrance. The lie of the inner channel is shown by a
convenient ferry. Buoy H3 is just visible under her port bow; the
buoy to her left in the picture is Hooksiel 1.

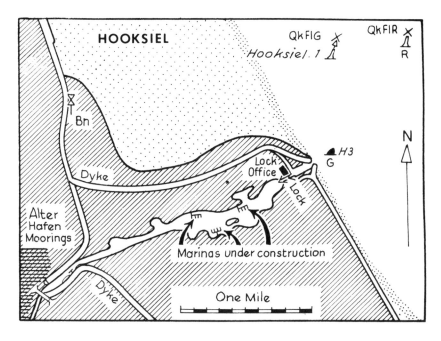

110

Hooksiel lock, arguably the best designed lock for yachts in
Europe, with pontoons with mooring bollards on both sides of
the lock. Seen from the lock office looking inland.

general depth of about 2.8 m. There are several private marinas, but probably the best bet is to carry on to the extreme SW end of the lake, where yachts can lie alongside in the Altenhafen. This is right in the middle of the little town, and there are shops and restaurants only a few yards away. Water from the marina pontoons; fuel was not observed in 1978, but will surely be available by the 1979 season, as the marinas grow.

I have rather a soft spot for Hooksiel, as when I visited it in 1978, sailing singlehanded in *Kuri Moana*, the lock-keeper told me that I was the first British visitor to pass through the new lock, and waived lock and harbour charges. He was a splendid character and spoke good English, so if he is still there (he can be recognised by a fringe of beard round a clean-shaven face) he will give advice about where to moor after locking through. But use the Altenhafen if possible: it is far more convenient than the marina berths, which are miles from anywhere.

Continuing south up the Jade from Hooksiel, there are three very large tanker loading piers built out nearly a mile into the river. The northernmost of these has an island unit offshore from the main pier: it is safe to pass between them if conditions make this desirable.

Hooksiel: the Altenhafen.

Wilhelmshaven

After the third tanker berth, the first basin of Wilhelmshaven comes into view. The yacht harbour is 2 miles beyond this entrance, in the Nassauhaven, the basin bounded by a curved breakwater and overlooked by a radio tower.

The yacht pontoon is in the northern bay of the harbour, and yachts berth on both sides of it. (There are also permanent moorings along the north quay, but these are not for visitors.) The SW side of

Wilhelmshaven, the Nassauhafen. The yacht pontoon can be seen between the pierheads; the radio tower is an excellent mark.

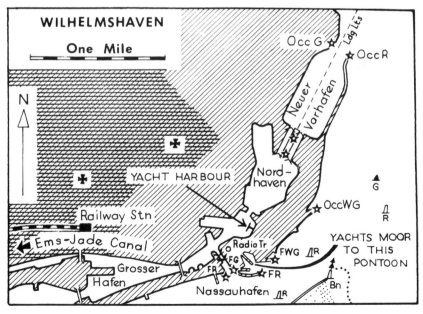

the pontoon is harder to see, and there is often a berth well up on this side when the NE side is full with three boats abreast. Water by hose; fuel from barge in the south bay, except on Sundays. Shops and restaurants in the town, about a mile away. This is a typical big-port yacht harbour, rather dirty and out of the way, and there seems little point in making the journey unless perhaps to change crews or undertake repairs. There are several inner harbours where yachts can lie by previous arrangement, so this would be a possible place to leave a yacht for a week or two. It is also the eastern end of the Ems-Jade Canal (see Appendix 5): access is via locks in the Neuer Vorhafen.

The Jadebusen
The Jade ends as a navigable river in this wide, shallow bay, which mainly dries at LW. It has two harbours: Dangastersiel, which is beautiful but overcrowded, and Varelersiel. The channel to Dangastersiel has $\frac{1}{2}$ m at LW springs, but the harbour dries and a visitor must risk finding no suitable berth. Varelersiel has a shallower approach, also dries, has even less room, and is not even a beauty spot, so for the intrepid I would recommend Dangastersiel of the two.

Passages from the Jade to the Weser
The main short-cut between Hooksiel or Wilhelmshaven in the Jade, and Bremerhaven in the Weser, is an extraordinary long watt-passage known as the Kaiserbalje. This branches eastward out of the Jade a couple of miles south of Hooksiel entrance, and winds for some 9 miles over the Hohe Weg, the great sandbank which divides the northern reaches of the two rivers, before reaching deep water in the Fedderwarder Priel, a branch of the main Weser.

Now let me make it quite clear that the general rule about watt-passages being calm and sheltered does not apply at all in this case. The watershed here is exposed from all directions except the south and in strong winds is very rough, and can be dangerous. Particularly in winds between NW and NE there is a heavy ground swell, and after having made the passage in a NW force 7 I will certainly never try it again in such conditions. With a heavy boat and a powerful engine I was just able to hold the courses, but it was a near thing, and if one had been swept off the line and driven aground the pounding that would have resulted would have broken up any yacht in a few minutes. I would say that the sensible limits are force 5 for winds between W and NE, and force 6 for other directions, although a southerly force 7 would be all right as long as it stayed there.

However, heavy weather is not all that common in the cruising season, and in good conditions this is a most useful channel. Approach from Jade buoy no. 40, about 2 hours before HW for preference (earlier rather than later); steer 100° M until the withies are sighted, when course can be altered to leave them close to port. There is a bar at the entrance of the Balje with about a metre at LW (2.8 m at half tide) after which the channel is deep for about 3 miles. Then the long shoal passage begins. The first watershed is the shallowest, about 1.7 m at HW neaps and 2.0 at HW springs; and it is most important to watch out for besoms (leave to starboard going E); there was one patch of besoms over a mile long in 1978.

After the first watershed, the channel reaches a deep, which is in fact the south end of the northern Kaiserbalje. This outlet is unmarked. The marked channel continues NE to the top of another unmarked channel, the Hundebalje, and then SE over the last watershed into the Fedderwarder Priel, just south of buoy F7. To reach the Weser proper, steer north along this buoyed channel to F1, and then east round the north end of the Leitdamm keeping on line for buoy no. 36, after which it is safe to turn SE down the main Weser.

From Wangersiel, or emerging from the Minseneroog channel, one may steer for the Mellumplate tower, then cut across into the Weser by passing close to the north of it, and then keep on a line between it and the Tegeler Plate light tower. Avoid being swept off the line by the cross-tide: once buoy Mellum 2 is reached it is safe to turn SE into the Weser. This passage can be used in worse conditions than the Hohe Weg passage (the Kaiserbalje), but should still be avoided in strong winds from the northern quadrant. The channel has 2.2 m at half tide.

Those who prefer to get a fair tide all the way can use neither of these passages, as each involves a foul tide in at least one of the rivers. They must sail down the Jade so as to pass the Schillighörn about $1\frac{1}{2}$ hours before LW. Keep north down the Mittelrinne past M3 and M4 to M2, which is also no. 7 Weser, and then turn ESE up the buoyed Weser channel. If the timing is right you will have come out of the Jade on the last of the ebb, and go up the Weser on the flood.

THE WESER

Compared with the Jade, the Weser has little to offer the visiting yachtsman. The channel is both narrower and more crowded, and

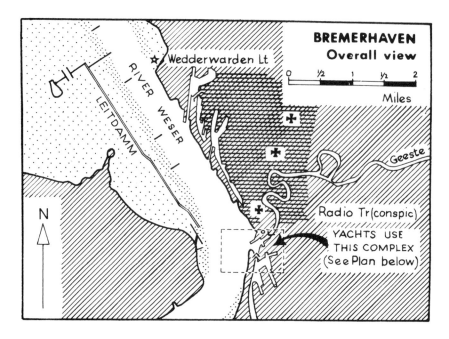

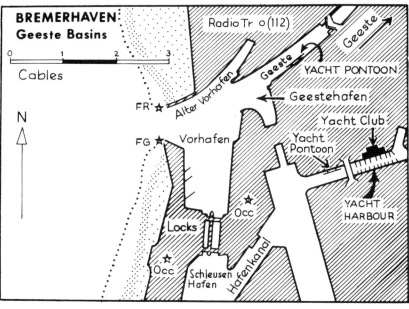

the first port is very much further from the open sea. However, the Hadelner Canal does offer a motor cruiser or yacht with lowering mast and maximum draft 1.5 m an alternative foul-weather route to the Elbe (Appendix 5), so it is worth covering as far as Bremerhaven, where the canal starts.

The entrance from the sea and the passages from the Jade have been dealt with above. Once in the channel, the buoyage is so generous that it would be hard to go wrong, but always allow for the very fast stream, which can reach four knots near Bremerhaven. It is therefore a slow business for the average yacht to make headway against the stream, which is one of the disadvantages of the Kaiserbalje, which entails a 12 mile slog into the ebb. It is better to try to work the tides: LW at the Alte Weser tower at the mouth of the river is $1\frac{1}{4}$ hours before LW Bremerhaven.

Bremerhaven

The entrance for yachts at Bremerhaven is the southernmost basin, whose entrance lies just south of the conspicuous 112 m radio tower. Yachts may moor to a pontoon on the south side of the Geeste, but this is only 30 m long and in 1978 was in poor condition. This basin, which is the second entrance on the north side of the complex, suffers from severe swell in W to SW winds and can be uncomfortable. If staying, it is far better to lock into the Schleusehafen through the locks at the south end of the Vorhafen. Sound **Q** ($---\cdot-$) to enter: go in when given green light. Once through, perform a

Bremerhaven from outside the entrance, looking straight up the Geeste. The locks are round to starboard.

Bremerhaven: *Kuri Moana* is moored outside the swing bridge
that leads to the yacht club basin. The luxurious club is in the
building to the left of and beyond the bridge.

hairpin turn to port through the Hafenkanal, and keep straight
across the Handelshafen (alas, I heard no Water Music there!) into
the Hauptkanal. Moor on the north side just before the bridge, and
arrange a berth with the yacht club, which will be found in an im-
posing building just beyond the bridge on its east side.

The yacht club is most hospitable, with a splendid bar, good food,
and excellent showers and toilets. It is closed on Tuesdays. Fuel may
be had from a bunker-barge in the Schleusenhafen, and of course the
large town offers all stores and facilities, including excellent
chandlers.

Entrance to the Hadelner Canal is through the bridge and lock at
the top of the Geeste basin; enquire at the Vorhafen locks for
arranging entry.

VI · The River Elbe

Charts: German 4 (from Weser only), 44, 45

The Elbe is the most important of the German rivers, as it is the one which gives access to the Kiel Canal (Nord-Ostsee Kanal) and the Baltic. However, it must always be remembered that for the small vessel, by which I mean anything under about 15 tons displacement, this can be a very dangerous estuary. The seas can be exceptionally steep and severe in wind-over-tide conditions, and more than one yacht attempting to enter with a following gale over the last of the ebb has been pitchpoled and lost. In strong W or NW winds, **on no account** proceed east of Elbe 1 lightvessel until the flood has begun.

The Elbe river is also one of the most crowded waterways in the world, and it would be most unwise to try to navigate it without reliable power. And a final warning: the buoyage is plentiful, but at night the sheer number of flashing lights makes it very difficult to identify individual marks, so I would advise all but the very experienced to avoid the river at night as far as possible, certainly until they know it reasonably well by day.

The Weser-Elbe watt-passage

Surprisingly few yachtsmen are aware of the fact that there is a shallow water passage that leads all the way from the Weser to the Elbe. This is well marked, easy to follow and sheltered, and I suppose the reason it is not better known is that it requires a minimum of two tides to complete, and therefore very often two days. However there are plenty of good anchorages in which the low-water period can be spent, and a couple of harbours if needed, so it seems a pity that the route is not better known.

From the west, the channel starts at buoy W10/Weser-Elbe 1. Coming from Bremerhaven, this is reached by the Wurster Arm (west cardinal buoys), which is the branch of the Weser running

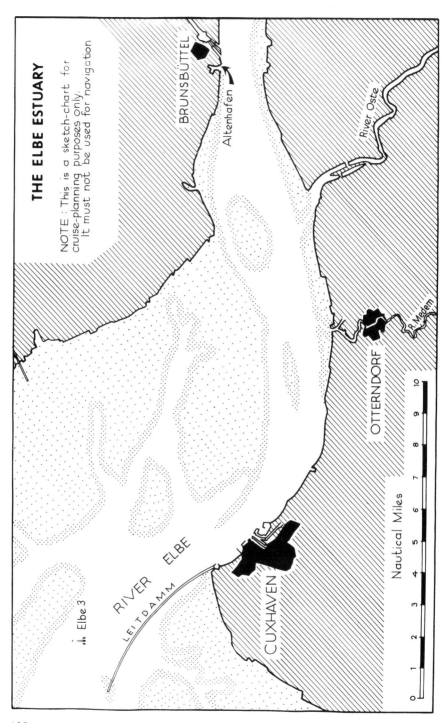

THE ELBE ESTUARY

NOTE: This is a sketch-chart for cruise-planning purposes only. It must not be used for navigation

BRUNSBÜTTEL

Altenhafen

River Oste

OTTERNDORF

R. Medem

Elbe 3

RIVER ELBE

LEITDAMM

CUXHAVEN

Nautical Miles

0 1 2 3 4 5 6 7 8 9 10

Crabbers' regatta at Cuxhaven.

north of the northern Leitdamm. From the west or seaward it is reached via the Dwarsgat from the main Weser. Both channels are well buoyed.

From W10 steer east for the withies, which lead over the first watershed, known as Meyers Legde. This dries over 1 m above water at LW, but has at least 1.7–2.0 m at HW. From here the channel turns north into deep water. After buoys WE6 and WE8, it turns NE again to WE10. Here one may turn N over another watershed, or continue NE and E for the harbour of Spieka-Neufeld.

Spieka-Neufeld
This small fishing harbour is too shallow to be a really useful stopping place on the Weser-Elbe watt-passage, as the depth at HW is only 1.5–1.8 m. However the shallow-draft yacht can often scrape out an hour or so before HW and get over the watersheds before the water runs out, and it is a valuable port of refuge in case of engine trouble or other breakdown. The entrance channel is marked by withies and besoms (leave to port and starboard

respectively), and yachts moor on jetties in a small bay on the north side of the harbour.

Most yachts, however, will turn north at buoy WE10 and take the marked channel over another watershed (2.0–2.3 m at HW) to WE12. From here a long deep-water channel leads first north and then east, and an anchorage must be found as there is no way that the last watershed, another 8 miles away, can be crossed on the same tide. In westerly winds the best anchorage is probably 100 m SW of buoy WE16; otherwise continue past the red and white Ostertill Weser-Elbe buoy and E along the Bakenloch to about 2 miles east of WE22, where there is a $2\frac{1}{2}$ mile length of sheltered channel shortly before the final watershed.

On the next tide (or in really exceptional conditions, or with a fast motor cruiser, the whole passage can be máde on one tide), proceed E from WE22, following the withies over the final watershed (leave them to port going E). This final watershed has 1.6 to 1.9 m at HW, sometimes a little more.

At this point the yacht is only 5 miles from Cuxhaven as the gull glides, but unfortunately the Leitdamm lies in the way, and the channel curves N and then NW after WE26 and must be followed up via WE28, NF9 and NF4 to the Mittelgrund W beacon. From here it is safe for a yacht to steer NE into the main channel of the Elbe, which is joined about $7\frac{1}{2}$ miles from Cuxhaven. Unfortunately the tide will now be ebbing, and in the fast stream this may take the average yacht another three hours or so to complete. Even so, it is a useful and interesting passage, and must be one of the longest of its kind in the world.

Approach and entrance to the Elbe

The main buoyed channel into the Elbe begins at Elbe 1 lightship, which lies exactly on the 54th parallel at 8° $06\frac{1}{2}'$E. It cannot be said too often that in strong winds from W or NW the entrance is dangerous when the ebb is running, and yachts arriving early should heave-to or jill around near Elbe 1 until LW which is about an hour before LW Cuxhaven (see Appendix 4).

Once the flood has begun entry is safe in all conditions, although getting out when a westerly gale is blowing is a more difficult matter, and indeed impossible for the ordinary yacht. The channel is well buoyed and needs no further comment except to say that it is one of the most crowded waterways in the world; yachts must keep to the starboard side of the channel, and preferably navigate just outside the channel buoys, in order to avoid inconveniencing commercial ships, which often have enough difficulty keeping out of each

The Grosser Vogelsand light in the Elbe. The object to the right
of the tower is one of the numerous wrecks with which the area
is littered.

other's way, particularly when overtaking. It is also worth mentioning that coming out against a more moderate W or NW wind,
the seas will be found to be at their worst between the Grosser
Vogelsand tower and buoy no. 4. Beware of plastic bags in this area!

Entering, once past the Grosser Vogelsand tower the channel
begins to become more sheltered, and once it has curved away to the
south past the red and white Elbe 3 buoy conditions are always
manageable, although the river can be wet and choppy as far up as
Brunsbüttel. The entrance to Cuxhaven lies 6½ miles beyond Elbe 3;
it was once a dreadful place for yachts but is now one of the most
comfortable cruising berths on the North Sea coast.

It seems unlikely to apply to most readers of this book, but it is
worth mentioning that anyone entering the Elbe without having
cleared Customs in Germany, and intending to pass through the Kiel
Canal, should fly the International Code Flag 3rd Substitute. Failure
to do this can result in being closely approached and hailed or even
boarded by a Customs launch while in the river. If cruising in
Germany this is unnecessary.

Cuxhaven

The approach from seaward presents no problem; the entrance to
the yacht harbour, clearly marked on the inset to chart 44, lies just
over a mile beyond the Kugelbake, a prominent beacon at the south

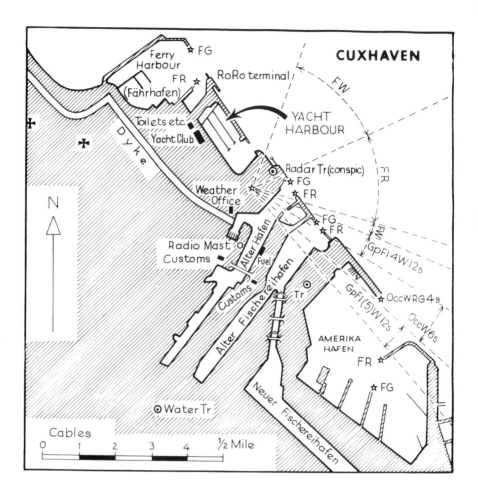

end of the Leitdamm, where it joins the land. The next prominent object on the shoreline is a conspicuous round radar tower, and the yacht harbour entrance is 100 m NW (i.e. to seaward) of this. The entrance had no navigational lights in 1978, but the whole area is brilliantly lit and it is quite easy to find at night.

Coming from the east, the yacht harbour lies beyond the main commercial basins, and the round radar tower once more acts as a useful mark. The difficulty here is that it is obligatory to keep to the starboard side of the channel in the Elbe, so when one has the entrance abeam it is necessary to cross the traffic streams in order to enter. This can be a tricky business as the river is often very crowded, and a close watch must also be kept for ships emerging from or diving into the various commercial basins.

Cuxhaven from the NW. The round tower just east of the entrance makes a good landmark in daylight. The Ro-Ro terminal bridge can be seen near the right of the picture: compare this view with the following photograph.

Cuxhaven: entrance to the yacht harbour. Enter between the three posts and the tower at the end of the Ro-Ro berth wall.

Once inside the yacht harbour entrance the extensive pontoon system will be seen on the starboard hand. The pontoons are new and well made, with water and electricity available. There is a yacht club open from 0900 to 2200 or later, good toilets, and a rather primitive shower operating on 50 pf pieces.

All stores are available in the considerable town, but it is over a mile before anything much is to be found. One of the few sailmakers in this part of the world is to be found here: enquire at the yacht club. Diesel can be bought from a BP station on a quay in the Altenhafen, the first basin after the yacht harbour when going SE; it is about halfway down the main basin on the east side.

Dues are rather high for the area (1978 rates were DM8 for 6–8 m LOA, and DM 10 for 8–10 m, for example), but the facilities are excellent, and anyone who endured the discomforts of Cuxhaven in the mid-1970s will probably think it well worth it.

Proceeding up the Elbe, the only harbour of much use to the yachtsman before Brunsbüttel is Otterndorf.

Otterndorf
Approach from buoy no. 45, from where a light beacon will be seen 3 cables to the SW. Allowing for the stream which can be 3 or 4 knots, steer to leave this close to starboard; the rest of the entrance channel is marked by besoms, also to be left to starboard when entering. Once inside the coastline the channel forks. Take the wider starboard fork, and proceed to the port-hand one of the two locks. Once through, pontoons will be seen on the west side: yachts lie two or three abreast. There is a friendly yacht club and a good restaurant nearby, but the nearest shops are over a mile away in the main village. Water available, but no fuel. The entrance channel carries just under 1 m of water at LW springs, and so is available to most yachts at practically all states of the tide.

River Oste
The only purpose of including this entry is to warn readers against anchoring in the outer part of this river. There is heavy traffic, the streams run strongly, and the holding is poor and often foul.

Brunsbüttel
It is of course possible for a yacht to sail up the Elbe as far as Hamburg, but for the purposes of this volume, Brunsbüttel is the end of the line. Here is the entrance to the Kiel Canal (Nord-Ostsee Kanal is the more recognisable name to the inhabitants of most European countries), the gateway to the Baltic.

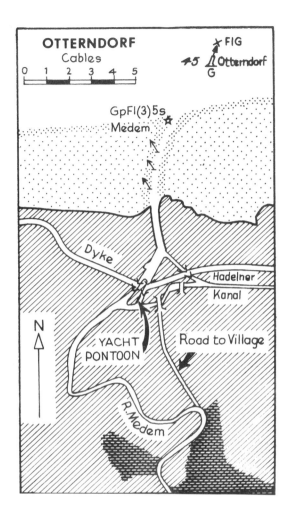

There are two yacht harbours: the Altenhafen outside the locks, and the main yacht harbour which is actually inside the canal.

The Altenhafen lies just to the west of the locks, its entrance channel marked by a beacon with an IALA west cardinal topmark of two cones with points together. At night, there are leading lights (Gp. Occ (3) red). Further in, the channel is marked by withies to port and besoms to starboard. There is a bar in the channel with about 0.4 m at LW springs, so with a mean range of 2.7 m there is about 1.7 m at half tide in the shallowest part of the channel. Depth is greater inside: about 1 m at LW springs alongside the 60 m long

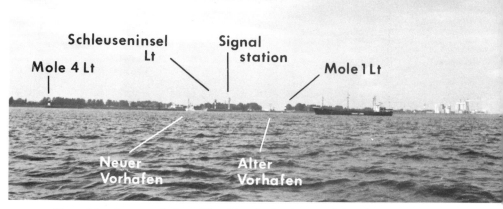

Brunsbüttel: general view. The Altenhafen is out of the picture to the left.

Brunsbüttel: Altenhafen entrance. From the beacon inwards the channel is marked by withies to port and besoms to starboard.

guest pontoon. The mud is soft, and keelboats sink in and stay upright. Dues in 1978 were DM4 per day for 7–10 m LOA, DM5 for 10–15 m. An additional tax of DM1.50 per boat per visit is charged for the upkeep of the beacon, but even so this is one of the cheapest berths in Germany, and a charming place it is. There are toilets and showers (50 pf) on the port side of the harbour; and a clubhouse on the starboard side has toilets and washbasin, but the club room is used only for lectures. Socially, the meeting place is in the café on the hill to the north of the harbour. Electric point by the club, and a

128

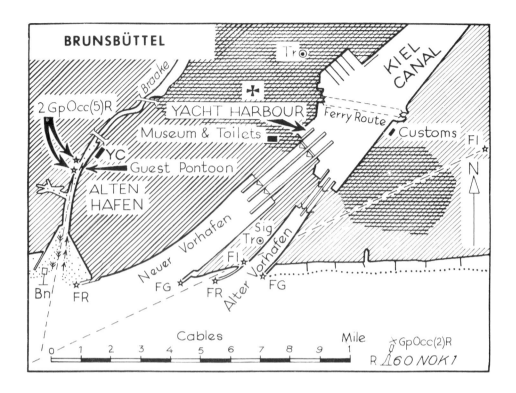

slip which will take vessels up to 2 m draft and 10 tons displacement. There is a playground, barbecue area and swimming pool nearby. Shops in the main village 500 m away.

Most visitors will be using the canal, however, and will lock in straight away. Yachts should wait to the east of the east mole until they see a single white light, and then enter the Vorhafen indicated. A further white light, shown from the lock, permits the yacht to enter. Many yachts do jill about just off the division between the two Vorhafens, and while this is against the strict regulations they are left alone as long as they keep entirely out of the way of all commercial shipping, but in strong winds it is an unwise practice. When waiting to *leave* the canal, yachts should jill on the far (NE) side of the ferry crossing until a single white light is shown. The locks do listen on VHF channels 13 and 9, which saves a lot of worry.

Once through the locks, which are easy to cope with as they have floating fender-booms to which a yacht can secure, the yacht harbour lies immediately NW of the most northwesterly lock. It is clean and well made but water is available only from a tap, or borrow a short hose from the harbourmaster. Good toilets will be found (un-

Brunsbüttel: canal yacht harbour, looking east.

Brunsbüttel: canal yacht harbour. The control lights for the new
locks can be seen in the centre of the photo, just to the right of
Kuri Moana's mast.

signposted) at the side of the museum in the wood, but male readers
should be warned that to sit down requires two 10 pf pieces. It's not
that it's expensive, but the exact change is needed. Good shower:
DM1, apply at the tobacco kiosk.

Diesel can be had at duty-free prices – a considerable saving –
from a rather inconspicuous Esso bunkerstation 250 m up the canal

on the port side. Petrol only from the garage on the way to the village, which has excellent shops and restaurants. The Yachthaven Café serves only snack food, but has interesting live music most evenings, played by the proprietor. Lock dues in 1978 were DM8 per locking up to 8 m LOA (DM15 through to the Baltic); DM10 (DM20) for 8–12 m; and DM20 (DM40) for boats over 12 m LOA. In addition, the yacht harbour charged DM6 per day for LOA 8–16 m.

THE KIEL CANAL (NORD-OSTSEE-KANAL)

A detailed essay on the navigation of the canal is outside the scope of this book. Suffice it to say that for pleasure boats, navigation at night is forbidden. When dark falls yachts must stop at the next permitted stopping-point: these are Dükerswisch (at Km 21.5) by the Gieselau Locks (entry at Km 40.5), the Obereidersee (entry at Km 66), Borgstedt narrows (entry Km 70), and the yacht anchorage in the Flemhudersee (entry Km 80.5). Each kilometre is marked by a large numbered sign: total length $98\frac{1}{2}$ Km. The locks at Holtenau, the Baltic end of the canal, use VHF channel 12.

Sailing yachts are allowed to motorsail in the canal, but the engine must be kept running at all times. Yachts may ignore light signals on the canal with the exception of three vertical red lights: if these are seen, stay where you are until the signal is switched off or changed. It usually means that an exceptionally large vessel is passing through one of the narrow stretches of the canal. Naturally, yachts should keep to the starboard side of the canal at all times, but do not go too close to the shore while being passed by a large ship, as the effect of the suction can be to throw a small boat towards the bank of the canal. The only practicable place for shopping is Rendsburg, off a branch to the north of the canal about 20 miles from Holtenau (entry about Km 62). A night (or longer) may be spent there.

Appendix 1 Weather Forecasts

The ordinary BBC Shipping Forecasts broadcast on 200 kHz (1500 m) can be picked up easily from anywhere in the area, and I have always found their detailed synopsis to be most useful, as it enables you to work out what is going on, even if the weather does not turn out exactly as predicted. These forecasts are transmitted at 0015, 0625, 1355 and 1750 UK local time: i.e. GMT in winter and BST (GMT + 1 hr) in summer. The whole of the area covered by the book lies within 'German Bight', but particularly at the west end of the area I have often found the forecasts for Humber to be more accurate.

I will follow *Reed's Almanac*'s example and give the times for European forecasts in GMT, because otherwise considerable confusion can arise, particularly when lying in Germany and listening to a Dutch forecast, or vice versa. Add one hour to the GMT times given to convert to German time, the same for Dutch time in the winter; but two hours for Dutch Summer Time, if it remains as it has in recent years.

The most popular service for the average British yacht is Scheveningen Radio, as their bulletins are either in English only, or in English and Dutch. The schedules are:

    421 kHz: 0918, 1518, 2118 GMT

    1862, 1939 or 2824 kHz: 0340, 0940, 1540, 2140 GMT

Forecasts for German Bight are also broadcast by Norddeich Radio in English on 474 kHz at 0800 and 2000 GMT.

Special forecasts for the Elbe can be obtained by telephone from Hamburg: tel. 1164.

I do not propose to list the numerous foreign-language forecasts, but I will just mention that both German and Dutch forecasters divide their forecasts into numbered areas called *Gebiets*. In Germany, *Gebeit Ein* is German Bight; in Dutch the same area is denominated *Gebeit Vijf* (meaning 5, pronounced '*fafe*').

Appendix 2 Radiotelephony by VHF

Being mainly very flat, the coasts covered by this book are ideal for VHF transmission and reception, and the standard of service provided by the coastal stations is in general very high.

In Dutch waters the only station is Scheveningen Radio, which covers the entire coast by means of a network of remotely controlled substations. Call on VHF channel 16, and you will be asked to stand by on another channel. Do *not* call again on that channel: wait until your turn, when you will be called up and your business taken care of. The most likely VHF channels to be needed here are 27 or 25.

One warning: Scheveningen usually asks a yacht for the name of its radio company. In fact, few people use one, as the service is rather expensive for the number of calls made from the average yacht. You will then be asked for your name and address, so take the precaution of having it, as well as your ship's name, written out in NATO radio alphabet, unless your facility with NATO letters is a good deal better than mine. If, however, you and your yacht appear in *Lloyd's Register of Yachts*, it is only necessary to say so. Finally, do be sure that you know your radio procedure well, and use it properly. Scheveningen are efficient and courteous, but always very busy, and they are apt to become either impatient or unaccountably deaf with yachtsmen who waste time on the air.

Germany, like England, is served by individual coastal radio stations. Cruising these waters, Norddeich Radio covers the German islands about as far as Spiekeroog, after which Elbe-Weser Radio takes over for the rest of the inshore cruising area; further out to sea, Helgoland Radio is often the best bet. All, of course, listen on VHF channel 16: working channels for Norddeich are 61, 25 and 28; for Elbe-Weser 23, 24, 26 and 28; and for Helgoland 3 and 27. Carry as many as possible, as particularly with Elbe-Weser different channels are used in different areas, and if you cannot use the right one reception is often less satisfactory.

Appendix 3 Radiobeacons

The area is extremely well covered by radiobeacons, and I do not propose to cover in detail the information given in *Reed's Almanac* or the Admiralty lists. A few comments, however, to supplement the basic facts. Whether the first passage is made to Ijmuiden or Den Helder there is a useful radiobeacon on which one can home: for Ijmuiden, its own beacon with a range of 30 miles; and for Den Helder, the Texel lightvessel some 14 miles west of the harbour, range 50 miles.

The beacons strung along the islands at Eierland (north Texel), Vlieland, Ameland, Borkum and Wangerooge can never, of course, be used indiscriminately for homing in bad visibility, as there are offshore shoals, but a study of the chart will often show that there is a safe direction from which they can be approached: thus, for example, Vlieland light can be approached on a magnetic course of between 90° and 160°, or Ameland between 210° and 240°. In calm weather, having sounded in and got a sight of land, it is then often possible to feel your way on soundings into harbour. If any sort of bad weather is combined with fog, however, the place to make for is Helgoland: get to the SE of the island and approach the radiobeacon on a course of 325° M, and if you do not see No. 1 buoy, which the course-line passes through, you will come up to the South Mole just west of the entrance while still in deep water. The Helgoland beacon has the great advantage for this purpose of being continuous as well as powerful.

Note that the beacons on Ameland and Eierland operate only in fog. However, for fixing your position there are plenty left: the group of six on 308 kHz usually turn out to be the most useful.

Appendix 4 Tides and Tidal Differences

In a cruising ground with so much shallow water, it is vital to know as accurately as possible what the tide is doing at any time and place. *Reed's Almanac* provides most of the basic information, but not always in the most convenient form: for example, the predictions for Harlingen are needed in order to use the stream atlas for the western Waddenzee, but in *Reed's* the Harlingen tides have to be found by time difference on Helgoland – printed in its Local Standard Time, but standard for Germany, not for the Netherlands in summer! For Dutch tides, most chandlers give away local tables, and there are tables for Harlingen in the back of Vol. 2 (Deel 2) of the *Almanak voor Watertoerisme*, which is an invaluable reference book, with times of bridge and lock openings, plans of harbours, and all manner of other information.

For Germany, a most useful booklet is the *Hoch-und-Niedrigwasserzeiten (Deutsche Bucht)*, issued by the German Hydrographic Institute at Hamburg. This is available from coastal bookshops and chandlers in Germany.

The very complex tidal streams of the area are mainly covered by two stream atlases, issued by the Dutch Hydrographic Office, and called *Stroomatlas Waddenzee, Westelijk* (West) and *Oostelijk* (East) *Deel*. The West volume was available in 1978; it was hoped that the East one would be ready for the 1979 season. They are available from J. D. Potter Ltd in London, or in the Netherlands from Harri or Datema (addresses in first Chapter).

For readers who have not had time to acquire the more detailed tide tables recommended above, I have prepared a list of tidal differences which make it possible to calculate the times of tides from HW Helgoland, which is supplied in *Reed's*. I have grouped these as differences on a main port, but also given the direct correction to the Helgoland tide, to reduce the amount of calculation required, and therefore the scope for error.

SW Waddenzee and Dutch Islands

	Difference on Harlingen	Difference on Helgoland*	Mean Tidal Range
Harlingen	0.00 hrs	−1.40 hrs	1.9 m
Den Helder	−2.21	−4.01	1.6
Oudeschild	−1.33	−3.13	1.5
Kornwerderzand	−0.16	−1.56	1.9
Vlieland (hbr)	−0.58	−2.38	2.0
Terschelling (hbr)	−0.24	−2.04	2.0
Nes (Ameland)	+0.25	−1.15	2.2
Schiermonnikoog (hbr)	+0.43	−0.57	2.4
Lauwersoog	+0.43	−0.57	2.4

German Islands

	Difference on Norderney	Difference on Helgoland	Mean Tidal Range
Borkum	−0.35 hrs	−1.00 hrs	2.3 m
Greetsiel	+0.23	−0.02	—
Norddeich	+0.09	−0.16	2.5
Norderney	0.00	−0.25	2.4
Nessmersiel	+0.20	−0.05	—
Baltrum	+0.14	−0.11	2.4
Dornumersiel	+0.28	+0.03	2.5
Bensersiel	+0.30	+0.05	2.5
Langeoog	+0.26	+0.01	2.6
Neuharlingersiel	+0.30	+0.05	2.5
Spiekeroog	+0.26	+0.01	2.7
Harlesiel	+0.32	+0.07	—
Wangerooge (hbr)	+0.33	+0.08	2.8

*Remember that *Reed's* gives Helgoland in Local (German) Standard Time: for Dutch Summer Time add 1 hour to the times in *Reed's* before applying the differences.

River Jade

	Difference on Wilhelmshaven	Difference on Helgoland	Mean Tidal Range
Wilhelmshaven	0.00 hrs	+ 1.05 hrs	3.7 m
Hooksiel	−0.26	+ 0.39	3.2
Wangersiel	−0.40	+ 0.25	—
Schillighörn	−0.37	+ 0.28	—
Mellumplate Lt Tr	−0.49	+ 0.16	2.9
Oldoog Lt	−0.59	+ 0.06	2.9
Jadeplate	−1.12	−0.07	—

River Weser

	Difference on Bremerhaven	Difference on Helgoland	Mean Tidal Range
Bremerhaven	0.00 hrs	+ 1.35 hrs	3.6 m
Fedderwardersiel	−0.23	+ 1.12	3.4
Hohe Weg Lt Tr	−0.55	+ 0.40	3.1
Dorumersiel	−0.58	+ 0.37	—
Alte Weser Lt Tr	−1.24	+ 0.11	2.8
Weser Lt vessel	−1.44	−0.09	—

River Elbe

	Difference on Cuxhaven	Difference on Helgoland	Mean Tidal Range
Brunsbüttel	+ 1.03 hrs	+ 2.23 hrs	2.7 m
Otterndorf	+ 0.27	+ 1.47	2.8
Cuxhaven	0.00	+ 1.20	2.9
Scharhörn bn	−0.54	+ 0.26	2.9
Elbe 1 Lt vessel	−1.12	+ 0.08	—

It should be noted that all tables of this kind involve a degree of compromise, and are approximations, but the figures given should enable the reader to judge the time of high water to within a few minutes. Mean range of the tide at Helgoland is 2.3 m. Tidal streams in the eastern rivers follow fairly closely the direction of the channels, and turn near enough at local high and low water, so the tables can be used to calculate the direction of the stream in the rivers as well as the depth of water.

Appendix 5 Inland Routes

Note: The first three routes described are available to yachts of normal size with mast in place.

Flushing to Amsterdam and Den Helder
This route does of course fall outside the scope of this book, but I include it for the benefit of those who prefer to avoid overnight sea passages. From Flushing yacht harbour the Kanaal door Walcheren leads north to Veere, a beautiful town with good yacht berths. Go east along the Versemeer and lock out at the other end, into the Ooster Schelde. (An alternative from Flushing to this point is to sail east up the Wester Schelde to Hansweert, and use the Kanaal door Zuid-Beveland which runs north into the Ooster Schelde.)

From here, the route runs NE past Zijpe, being tidal until just before Willemstad, where there are large locks, the ones for yachts being on the NW side. After the pretty town of Willemstad, proceed up the Hollandse Diep and the Dordsche Kil to Dordrecht, where there is a railway bridge which can cause considerable delays; yacht harbours are beyond on the east side up a side canal. Go on past Alblasserdam Bridge into the Nieuwe Maas; follow this NW for 6 miles, and then turn sharp to starboard up the Hollandse Ijssel. (If bad weather has improved by here, one can go straight on instead, coming out at Hook of Holland, and take the sea route north to Den Helder, with possible stops at Scheveningen and/or Ijmuiden.)

Shortly before Gouda, turn to port through the Julianasluis, and proceed by Alphen and Oude Wetering to Schiphol. The bridge here opens only at 0500–0630, 1230–1330, and 2000–2100. From here pass through the Nieuwe Meer and on into Amsterdam. The railway bridge here opens only at 0215.

Once out into the Noordzeekanaal, one has another chance to return to the sea, sailing out from Ijmuiden with only the short and straightforward run to Den Helder to cover. Otherwise one may turn

138

north just east of the railway bridge west of Amsterdam, and go north up the Noordhollands Kanaal to Den Helder, or turn east to the Ijsselmeer and lock out into our cruising ground at Den Oever or Kornwerderzand.

For the southern part of this route proper charts are needed: the easiest to use being the Dutch Yacht Charts 1803, 1805, 1807 and 1809 (1803 is only needed if going by Hansweert). For the rest of the canal system I have always managed with *Born's Schipperskaart*, but there are more detailed canal charts available: ANWB *Waterkaart* F, G, H, I and J cover the route. (All these are available in the UK through J. D. Potter, and shown on the ANWB map *Vaarwaterkaart van Nederland*.) Motoring at five knots, and travelling non-stop from dawn to dusk, it is just possible to get from Flushing to Amsterdam by the inland route in two days. The Noordhollands Kanaal can be covered comfortably in one day, but unless there is great urgency I would suggest allowing four days for the whole trip as a minimum for comfortable cruising. The *Almanak voor Watertoerisme, Deel 2 (Vol. 2)* should be carried for up-to-date information on bridge opening times, etc. It is in Dutch, but opening times are clearly set out against the bridge or lock, so it presents little difficulty.

Harlingen to Lauwersoog
From Harlingen, the van Harinxmakanaal leads east through Franeker to Leeuwarden. Turn north as the town is reached, and continue along the Dokkummer Ee to Dokkum, and then by the Dokkumergrootdiep to the locks at Nieuwezijlen. Lock out into the Lauwersmeer, and proceed to Lauwersoog (this section is covered on chart 1812). This is a straightforward route with no slow bridges: it can be done in one day without difficulty, but an early start is advisable.

Lauwersoog to Delfzijl
Proceed from Lauwersoog to the locks at Zoutkamp in the SE corner of the Lauwersmeer. (This route can of course be combined with the one above by cutting across from Nieuwezijlen to Zoutkamp.)

These locks give access to the Reitdiep, which leads slowly but without problems to Groningen (see inset on chart 1812.3 or sea chart 1555). This town is usually slow to pass through, unless you are lucky enough to get behind a big barge: if you are, it is worth following through the first of the Eemskanaal bridges even if there is shopping to be done: it is quite a short walk back into town, and one can moor conveniently just past the bridge.

The remainder of the distance is covered by the Eemskanaal: almost straight and with few bridges. Approaching Delfzijl, the canal forks: yachts should keep to the starboard (S) arm.

As with the previous section, this trip can comfortably be completed in one day, but it is advisable to be under way before 0900.

Emden to Wilhelmshaven

This route, the Ems-Jade Kanal, is available only to vessels with lowering masts or none at all. It provides for boats with draft up to 1.7 m, and the bridges have a least clearance of 3.75 m. The length of the canal is 39 nautical miles, but with six locks to negotiate one is unlikely to be able to get through in one day. Dues are fairly heavy, and although the canal is pretty it is little used by yachtsmen; I would mainly recommend it as a way of making ground towards home if the weather is really bad. If you do use it, keep out towards the middle where possible: depths tend to shoal considerably closer to the banks. There is a speed limit of 8 km/hr (about 4 knots) for drafts up to 1 m, and 5 km/hr ($2\frac{1}{2}$ knots!) for deeper-draft boats. This is not strictly enforced for yachts, but certainly speed should be kept well down.

Bremerhaven to Otterndorf (on the Elbe)

Included for completeness, this canal (the Hadelner Kanal) has a depth of only 1.5 m, and clearance above water of only 2.8 m. There are four locks (one usually open) and a 6 km/hr limit. Enter via the Geeste at Bremerhaven: total length to Otterndorf $32\frac{1}{2}$ N.M.

Appendix 6 Foreign Abbreviations and Glossary

CHART ABBREVIATIONS

Light Characteristics	*English*	*Dutch*	*German*
Fixed	**F**	**V**	**F**
Flashing	**Fl**	**S**	**Blz**
Long Flash	**L Fl**	**LS**	**Blk**
(Very) Quick Flashing	**(V) Qk Fl**	**Fl**	**(S) Fkl**
Isophase	**Iso**	**Iso**	**Glt**
Occulting	**Occ**	**O**	**Ubr**
Group Occulting (3)	**Gp Occ (3)**	**GO (3)**	**Ubr (3)**
Group Flash (3)	**Gp Fl (3)**	**GS (3)**	**Blk (3)** or **Blz (3)**

Note: Dutch Yachting Charts now use English abbreviations. Those shown above appear on the marine (sea) charts, in the *Almanak*, etc.

Colours	*English*	*Dutch*	*German*
Black	**B**	**Z**	**s**
Blue	**Bl**	**B**	**bl**
White	**W**	**W**	**w**
Red	**R**	**R**	**r**
Green	**G**	**Gn**	**gn**
Yellow	**Y**	**G**	**g**
Orange	**Or**	**Gl**	**or**

Beware of confusion between black and blue; or green, yellow and orange.

USEFUL DUTCH WORDS

Dutch is a difficult language for foreigners to pronounce, but it is worth trying to learn to say names reasonably well, as even good English speakers sometimes fail to understand place-names if they are grossly mispronounced.

oe should be pronounced as the **oo** in moon, **ei** as in height, **ie** as in bel*ie*ve, **ee** as the **a** in mate, and **ij** (the most difficult of all) nearly as the **a** in mate, but with a touch of the **i** in life. **Ij** counts as **Y** for alphabetical purposes, and is sometimes printed ÿ.

Aanlegplaats	Berth	Droogvallend	Drying (sand
Afval	Rubbish		etc)
Ankerplaats	Anchorage	Geen	No, none
Bakboord	Port (side)	Gemiddelde	Average
Bake	Beacon	Gesloten	Closed
Bedient	Manned	Getijtafel	Tide table
Benzine	Petrol	Gevaarlijk	Dangerous
Betonde	Buoyed,	Halftij	Half tide
	marked	Havengeld	Harbour dues
Betonning	Buoyage	Havenmeester	Harbourmaster
Beweegbare	Opening	Ingang	Entrance
	(bridge)	Jacht (haven)	Yacht (harbour)
Binnen	Inner	Meerboei	Mooring buoy
Brug	Bridge	NAP*	(see note below)
Buiten	Outer	Niet	Not
Diepte	Depth, draft	Ondiep	Shoal
Dieselolie	Diesel oil	Oost (O)	East (E)
Doodtij	Neap tide	Slang	Hose
Doorvaart-	Headroom	Sluis	Lock
hoogte		Snelheid	Speed
Douane	Customs	Spoorbrug	Railway bridge

*NAP or Normaal Amsterdams Peil—in practice equivalent to the average water level at mean tide. However, it must always be remembered that the water levels in the tidal inland water systems of the Netherlands (and elsewhere) are considerably affected by rainfall as well as tide. Thus after a period of prolonged rain the tides will oscillate about a noticeably higher mean, and in a drought about a lower one.

142

Springtij	Spring tide	Verboden	Forbidden
Stuurboord	Starboard	Vluchthaven	Harbour of refuge
Ton	Navigational buoy	Wantij	Watt water-shed
Touw	Rope		
Vaargeul	Fairway	Wassalon	Launderette
Vaarwater	Channel	Zuid (Z)	South (S)
Vast (brug)	Fixed (bridge)	Zwart (Z)	Black (B)
Veer	Ferry		

USEFUL GERMAN WORDS

Ankerplatz	Anchorage	Halbetide	Half tide
Anlegen	Mooring	Heuler	Whistle
Ausgang	Way out	Hochwasser	High tide
Backbord	Port (side)	Kaje	Quay
Bake	Beacon, post	Kartennull	Chart datum
Benzin	Petrol	Kein	No, none
Bewegliche	Opening (bridge)	Kette	Chain
		Leucht	Light
Brücke	Bridge, jetty	Liegeplatz	Berth
Damm	Breakwater	Niedrigwasser (NW)	Low tide
Deich	Dyke		
Eingang	Entrance	Nippzeit	Neap tide
Fähre	Ferry	Ort	Place, locality
Fahrt	Journey, passage	Ost (O)	East (E)
		Pfeiler	Pier
Fahrwasser	Channel, fairway	Priel	Narrow channel
		Revier	District
Festland	Mainland	Rinne	Narrow channel
Feuer	Light(house)	Schlauch	Hose
Flach	Shallow, flat	Schleuse	Lock
Funkfeuer	Radiobeacon	Schutzgebiet	Restricted area
Glocke	Bell	Sichtigkeit	Visibility
Hafenkapitän	Harbourmaster		

143

Siel	Sluice	Untiefe	Shoal
Springzeit	Spring tide	Veränderlich	Changeable
Steuerbord	Starboard	Verboten	Forbidden
Strömung	Current	Wassertiefe	Depth
Sturm	Gale	Wattenhoch	Watt watershed
Tauwerk (or Tau)	Rope	Wetterberich	Weather forecast
Tidenhub	Tidal Range	Zoll	Customs
Tonne	Buoy	Zufahrt	Approach
Trockenfallend	Drying (sand etc)		

Note: Both the above Glossaries have deliberately been kept short and put in alphabetical order of the foreign words, to assist the reader who encounters these words on notices, in the *Almanak* etc. *Reed's Almanac* provides a longer and more detailed list in both languages grouped under subjects, including shoregoing, for more leisurely use, and the symbols, words and chart abbreviations printed in the key to the Dutch Yacht Charts will also repay study.

Appendix 7 Bibliography

Charts are of course the first essential, and they have been dealt with in detail in the first chapter. I have designed this book so that it is possible to sail the area with no other reference but the charts and *Reed's Almanac*. However, the following, in many cases mentioned elsewhere, would be well worth their place in the bookshelf. All are available through J. D. Potter, with the possible exception of the German Tide Tables.

Almanak voor Watertoerisme (Deel 2) (pub. ANWB). Gives details of bridge and lock opening times in the Netherlands, and much other valuable information.

Die Nordseeküste: Elbe bis Ijsselmeer by Karlheinz Neumann (pub. Delius Klasing). A yachtsman's pilot in German covering the whole area and the Ijsselmeer. An extraordinary amount of information (not all of it accurate), interlarded with history and anecdote. The language is highly idiomatic, so not for linguistic beginners!

The Dutch Tidal Atlases and the German Tide Tables for Deutsche Bucht (see Appendix 4).

The Cruising Association Handbook (pub. Cruising Association). This massive collection of harbour plans and sailing directions, which I now edit, also gives details of Dutch inland waterways, and sailing directions for the possible ports of entry which lie outside the area of this book. Available J. D. Potter, or direct from the C.A., Ivory House, St Katharine Dock, London E1 9AT.

Barge Country by John Liley (pub. Stanford Maritime, late 1979). An illustrated and comprehensive guide to exploring the great rivers and canals of the Netherlands, Belgium and bordering areas of Germany and France.

Born's Schipperskart of Netherlands rivers and canals, other maps and cruising guides for Continental inland waters, and yachting pilot books are also available from Stanford's Map Shop, 12–14 Long Acre, London WC2E 9LP (tel 836 7863).

The Riddle of the Sands by Erskine Childers

A Thirst for the Sea: The Sailing Adventures of Erskine Childers by Hugh Popham (pub. Stanford Maritime late 1979).

Notes

Index

Frisian Pilot

Oldoog Lt 96
Oort 53
Oosterems, *see* Osterems
Oostmahorn 52
Oost Vlieland, *see* Vlieland
Oste River 126
Osterem 47
Osterems 58, 64–5, 67
Otterndorf 126, 140
Otzumer Balje 86, 89–90
Oudeschild 33–5

Pesensrede 48
Pieterburenwad 55
Pinkegat 48
Pollendam 33

Ra River 55
Radio (VHF) 133
RDF Beacons 134
Reitdiep 52, 139
Rendsburg 131
Riffgat 71, 74
Robbengat 55
Rotterdam 24
Roter Sand Lt 105

Schelde River 24
Scheurrak 32
Scheveningen 24, 138
Schiermonnikoog 19, 42, 49–50
Schillbalje 87, 88, 90
Schilphol 138
Schluchter 74
Schuitengat 33, 45
Smeriggat 48
Spieka-Neufeld 121–2
Spiekeroog 87–8, 90
Spiekerooger Wattfahrwasser 90
Spuit 53
Stortemelk 18, 40

Tegelerplate Lt 115
Telegraphenbalje 96
Terschelling 13, 18, 19, 21, 32,
  33, 40, 42, 43, 45–7

Texel 13, 25
Texelstroom 32, 33
Thomas Smit Gat 40
Tides 21, 22, 32, 135–7, 145

Vaarwater van de Zwarte
  Haan 47, 48
Varelersiel 114
Veerbotgat 48
Veere 138
Visjagersgaatje 32
Vlakte van Oostbierum 32, 47
Vlieland 13, 19, 33, 40, 42, 43–5
Vliestroom 32, 33
Vlieter 32

Waddenzee 13, 19, 21, 30–3
Wagengat 74
Wangerooge 19, 22, 87, 90, 91–3,
  96, 107
Wangersiel 108–9, 115
Weather forecasts 132
Weser River 18, 19, 23, 97, 105,
  114, 115–8
Weser LV 105
Weser-Elbe Wattfahrwasser
  119–122
Westeraccumersiel 84
Westerbalje 86
Westerems 18, 55, 58
Westgat (Zeegat van Ameland) 40
Westgat (Friesche Zeegat) 55
Westgat (Zeegat van Texel) 25,
  27
West Meeps 47
Wichter Ee 74, 77
Wierbalg 32
Wilhelmshaven 19, 23, 107, 108,
  113–14, 140
Willemstad 138

ÿ *see footnote*

Zeegat van Ameland 40
Zeegat van Terschelling 40
Zeegat van Texel 20
Zijpe 138

Note: Dutch words beginning with **ij** have been treated in this Index according to English alphabetical rules. However, readers should note the fact that in the Dutch language, and therefore in publications such as the ANWB *Almanak voor Water-toerisme*, **ij** is treated as **y** for listing purposes. Particularly in capitals the form ÿ is sometimes used instead of **ij**: there is no distinction between the two usages. The letter **y** without umlaut does not exist.